BSCI **105**

Introduction to Experimental Biology

Fall 2011–Spring 2012

Laboratory Manual

*Eds. Michael J. Keller
and Pamela J. Lanford*

University of Maryland–College Park

HAYDEN
HM
MCNEIL

Printed in the United States of America

10 9 8 7 6 5 4 3 2 1

ISBN 978-0-7380-4551-1

Hayden-McNeil Publishing
14903 Pilot Drive
Plymouth, MI 48170
www.hmpublishing.com

Keller 4551-1 F11

Table of Contents

BSCI 105

Contributors

Patricia Escobar-Paramo	*Department of Cellular and Molecular Biology, University of Maryland College Park, MD 20742*
Curtis Gilliam	*College of Chemical and Life Sciences, University of Maryland College Park, MD 20742*
Paul Gross	*Biological Sciences, University of Maryland College Park, MD 20742*
William Higgins	*Dept. of Biology, University of Maryland College Park, MD 20742*
Christina Kary	*Department of Cellular and Molecular Biology, University of Maryland College Park, MD 20742*
Michael Keller	*College of Chemical and Life Sciences, University of Maryland College Park, MD 20742*
Pamela Lanford	*Biological Sciences, University of Maryland College Park, MD 20742 E-mail: planford@umd.edu*
Tammatha O'Brien	*Biological Sciences, University of Maryland College Park, MD 20742*
Steven Spilatro	*Dept. of Biology, Marietta College Marietta, OH 45750 E-mail: spilatrs@marietta.edu*
Katerina Thompson	*Biological Sciences, University of Maryland College Park, MD 20742*

Special Contributor

Susan Hepp, an undergraduate teaching assistant, initiated and developed much of the content for Exercise 10, the PCR lab, which was the basis for the current DNA module.

Welcome

Welcome to BSCI 105 Laboratory!

The laboratory portion of Principles of Biology I is designed to complement the lecture materials and provide hands-on experience with fundamental tools of experimental science. This course will focus on molecular and cell biological processes. Throughout the coming semester we will accomplish four principal goals:

1. To become familiar with common laboratory equipment and the application of modern biological techniques.

2. To demonstrate fundamental concepts in molecular and cellular biology.

3. To learn how to apply the Scientific Method to biological problems.

4. To gain experience with basic scientific communication.

Your progress in accomplishing these goals will be assessed throughout the semester using worksheets, quizzes and writing assignments. You will also make and present a scientific poster that demonstrates your ability to understand and explain molecular and cell biological experiments from the literature. Finally, at the end of the semester you will be expected to demonstrate your ability to use laboratory equipment and carry out procedures covered by the laboratory exercises in a practical exam.

Keep in mind, this is a course designed for *science majors* to provide experiences that lay the groundwork for future coursework in the physical and life sciences. You will be expected to have or obtain a familiarity with certain concepts and knowledge not directly covered by the laboratory exercises.

If you come on time and fully prepared for the laboratory exercises each week, follow all instructions and put an honest effort into the graded assignments (and complete them on time), you should find this a straightforward, valuable and, hopefully, interesting experience.

Good Luck,
The BSCI 105 Laboratory Staff

Introduction to the Laboratory

BSCI 105 Laboratory Instructional Staff

A Graduate Teaching Assistant (TA) will be your principal instructor for the laboratory portion of BSCI 105. This is the person you will see on a regular basis and should be the first person you go to for help with the laboratory or lecture. All of the TAs will have posted office hours, and you can go to any TA for general help having to do with the content of the laboratory or lecture material. For more specific questions, please make an appointment with your section TA.

The Lab Manager is responsible for all technical aspects of the laboratory exercises and is the laboratory Safety Officer. The Lab Manager will monitor the laboratory sections and ensure the Rules of the Laboratory and other safety procedures are being followed.

The Lab Coordinator is responsible for administration of laboratories and coordination of the TAs. If you have questions about the laboratory exercises or assignments that are not adequately addressed by your TA, please make an appointment to discuss them with the Lab Coordinator.

Student Information Sheet

Please fill out the Student Information section of the sheet on page xv. Throughout the semester there will be occasions where your TA may need to contact you. In addition, the information you provide will help your TA to get to know you as an individual and the class as a whole.

Rules of the Laboratory

This and other laboratory courses are experiential in nature, require you to understand significant background on a variety of topics, and only work if everyone follows procedures. In addition, there are serious safety concerns associated with all laboratories that entail strict guidelines that must be followed at all times.

Please read the Rules of the Laboratory carefully and sign the sheet on page xvi. By signing this form, you are attesting to your familiarity with the rules and understanding that they must be strictly adhered to.

Code of Academic Integrity

All students of the University of Maryland are expected to adhere strictly to the Code of Academic Integrity. The Code is taken very seriously and violating it can have serious consequences.

Please read the University of Maryland Code of Academic Integrity thoroughly and sign the sheet on page xvi. Your signature signifies your understanding of the Code and agreement to abide by its principles. Hand in the completed signature sheet to your TA.

Laboratory Syllabus

You should receive a copy of the *lab syllabus* (also available on ELMS/ Blackboard) providing important information about the laboratory portion of BSCI 105. You are expected to read it thoroughly and be familiar with its contents. The syllabus includes a schedule for all of the laboratory exercises including assignment due dates and point values. You are expected to check the syllabus weekly and come to lab fully prepared and ready to go.

Online Resources

The lecture and laboratory portions of BSCI 105 each make extensive use of online resources available through ELMS/Blackboard (http://elms.umd.edu/), as will numerous other courses you will take at UMD. ELMS/Blackboard will be used to post documents, make announcements, track your grades, access other Web-based resources, and communicate with your instructors and classmates. In BSCI 105 you will actually have access to three different "course spaces":

- A *lecture* course space, where you will find materials posted by your professor and grades for certain assignments particular to your lecture. If you want to send an e-mail to everyone in your lecture section, you can do that from here.

- A *lab section* course space, where you will find materials specific to your lab section and your grades for lab assignments and lecture exams. You will also find links and quizzes for the MathBench material (see below). If you need to send an e-mail to everyone in just your lab section, you can do that from here.

- A *lab resources* course space, where you will find general resources or items posted by the Lab Coordinator during the semester. The most important materials available through this space will be the electronic reserve items you will need for your lab report later in the semester.

MathBench

The MathBench program is designed to ensure you are familiar with the quantitative concepts you will need to complete the BSCI 105 lab exercises and understand what you are doing and why. You will be asked to review a series of MathBench Modules throughout the semester, each with information relevant to the upcoming lab. In addition, you will be required to complete the associated quizzes as part of your lab preparation. The MathBench Modules and Quizzes are available through your lab section course space on ELMS/Blackboard.

BSCI 105

The Rules of the BSCI 105 Laboratories

1. As a CORE course, BSCI 105 requires your attendance in the lab classes. You MUST attend lab and you MUST be on time! Failing to attend lab has serious ramifications. *If you miss four or more labs during the semester, FOR ANY REASON, you fail the course.*

2. Students who are more than *five minutes* late will not be admitted to the classroom and will receive an unexcused absence.

3. If you miss a lab with a **valid** excuse, you may make up the points associated with the lab. Makeup work must be arranged through your TA. Only documented excuses will be accepted. Valid excuses include: religious holiday, collegiate sporting event, illness, death in the family, and unavoidable court appearance. Absences for pre-planned events (such as religious holidays) *must* be brought to the attention of your TA or the lab coordinator **within the first two weeks of lab.** Please see the lab Web site and syllabus for further details.

4. Assignments are due at the beginning of the class period unless specifically stated otherwise in the syllabus. Assignments turned in after the beginning of class will be considered late and may not be accepted by the TA. The TA will decide when and if makeup work will be allowed (if you wish to discuss a specific case—see the Lab Coordinator).

   Note: "Problems with my computer" (including problems with the printer) is not a valid excuse for late work.

5. Students are **NOT** to leave lab until they have cleaned up and are dismissed by the TA. Anyone leaving lab without the TA's permission will lose the points associated with that lab, and receive an "unexcused absence" for that lab period.

6. No eating or drinking is allowed in lab. Many chemicals used in lab are harmful if ingested.

7. No children may be brought to lab.

8. Shoes with closed toes must be worn in lab. No sandals, skates, rollerblades are allowed.

9. No electronic devices may be used during the lab period, including cell phones and laptop computers. You may not leave the lab to place a phone call.

10. Cheating in any form will not be tolerated. This includes plagiarism. You may work with a partner during the lab, however you are expected to do the outside assignments on your own and turn in original work.

    Plagiarism: intentionally or knowingly representing the words OR ideas of another as one's own in any academic exercise.

11. Abusive behavior of any kind to anyone associated with BSCI 105 will not be tolerated.

University of Maryland Code of Academic Integrity

Biology Program Policy

The University of Maryland–College Park has a nationally recognized Code of Academic Integrity, administered by the Student Honor Council. This Code sets standards for academic integrity at Maryland for all undergraduate and graduate students. As a student, you are responsible for upholding these standards. The lab instructors will proctor all quizzes for cheating and will monitor all assignments for academic dishonesty. All students found breaking the Code will be referred to the Student Honor Council.

Remember

While we encourage group work and thought in the laboratories, all written assignments produced in lab *or* outside of lab are to be the original work of the individual. Lab reports and other written assignments that are very similar in wording and organization will be considered plagiarism and referred to the Student Honor Council.

Definitions from the Code of Academic Integrity in your undergraduate catalog:

ACADEMIC DISHONESTY

Any of the following acts, when committed by a student shall constitute academic dishonesty:

- Cheating: intentionally using or attempting to use unauthorized materials, information, or study aids in any academic exercise.

- Fabrication: intentional and unauthorized falsification or invention of any information or citation in an academic exercise.

- Facilitating Academic Dishonesty: intentionally or knowingly helping or attempting to help another to violate any provision of this Code.

- Plagiarism: intentionally or knowingly representing the words or ideas of another as one's own in any academic exercise.

Lab Report Guide

Additional information about writing your lab reports can be found on the course Web page. It is strongly recommended that you familiarize yourself with all of the available materials.

When you think about "doing science," what comes to mind? If you are like most people, the three things that immediately pop up will be (1) making observations, (2) coming up with new ideas, and (3) doing experiments. While these are certainly major parts of any scientific endeavor they are *worthless* if all of those valuable observations, ideas and data are not communicated to the public. The presentation and publication of new concepts and experimental results are critical components of the scientific process as well. Typically, scientists communicate with one another and with the public at large through talks, poster presentations, and papers. As a science student participating in the BSCI 105/106 laboratories, you will be asked to communicate with your instructor through **lab reports** that are similar to scientific papers.

Don't panic! This isn't as daunting as it sounds. Luckily, scientists (and publishers) like to use consistent formats for their communications, and for the most part they organize their posters and papers in parallel with the "scientific method." That would be the same scientific method you have probably heard about before, which is used to conceive, design, and execute experiments. So, if you understand the scientific method, you should have little trouble putting together a lab report or poster (or the other way around). Let's compare the components of the scientific method to the format of a typical scientific paper:

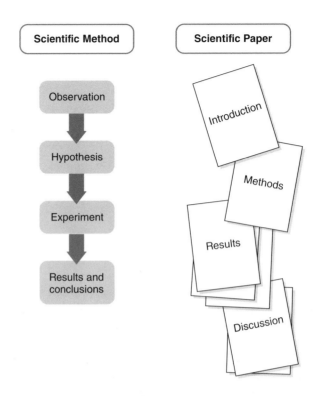

The laboratory reports for BSCI 105/106 will be written in the form of a typical life sciences journal article. This basic format is utilized by many professional journals because it provides a consistent mechanism for reporting the "why," "how," "what happened," and "so what, who cares" of an experiment in a concise and orderly fashion. Below are specific items you should keep in mind when writing the different components of your lab report.

Lab Report Format and Style Guide

Professional scientific journals require every author to follow *their* particular format exactly, and so will we. This is not difficult; it simply requires that you pay attention to detail. A component of your lab report grade will reflect the extent to which you follow these guidelines.

GENERAL FORMAT

- Font: Use Times 12, double-spaced
- 1″ margins on top, bottom, and sides
- Page numbers in lower right-hand corner
- Use metric units
- Label the Introduction, Methods, Results, Discussion, and Literature Cited sections

LENGTH

Most lab reports that are efficiently written are about 4–5 pages in length (not counting figures). The length of a given section will vary, depending on the exercise, but a rough outline for each is given below. These are, of course, **guidelines,** and the correct answer to "How long should my lab report be?" should be "As long as it needs to be." Your report should be sufficiently long to clearly explain all of the necessary information. Lab reports that are too long can be recognized by their wordiness and excess of irrelevant information.

NUMBERS

When you are writing numbers in your text: the Council of Science Editors says that you should use numerals (not words) when writing about counted or measured items, percentages, decimals, magnifications, and abbreviated units of measurement—except use the word if beginning a sentence (or better yet, reword so that doesn't happen).

SPECIES NAMES

Species names must be *italicized*. For example, *Drosophila melanogaster* is a species, therefore you need to have it fully written out and italicized at minimum once in your Title, Introduction, and Methods. You can then either refer to it as *D. melanogaster* or when you state it the first time, follow with (fruit flies) and use that for the rest of the report. Calling them *Drosophila* is like calling us *Homo*—it's not really enough information.

Contents by Section

TITLE

The contents of your paper should be adequately described by a short title (one line) that is simple, precise, and descriptive of your experiment. Avoid vague titles such as "An investigation of fruit flies." If you're assessing the relationship of wing size and selection, say so in the title. For example, "Substance Q alters the mitochondrial structure of Borborygmi tree squab blood cells." You may have no idea what that means, but after reading the title you can infer that a researcher interested in Substance Q, tree squabs, blood cells, or mitochondria might want to read this journal article. Also, if you're working with just one or two species, it is useful to include the scientific names (check spelling!) of the organisms in the title.

You may *not* simply rewrite the title of the exercise in this manual; your title *must* be original.

Look at some other titles in scientific journals to get an idea of what they look like.

ABSTRACT

The abstract is the most widely read portion of the paper. You must efficiently summarize your study to enable readers to decide if they want to read further. The abstract is usually written last, and should be no more than 300 words. It should include:

- A sentence or two about the general nature and importance of the problem (the "why")
- The specific questions you address (the "what")
- The methods used (the "how")
- *Principal* results as they relate to the central question(s) (the "what happened")
- Your conclusions (the "so what, who cares")

NOTE: This section is typically written using the passive voice.

Please remember, the abstract is a *paragraph* that needs to read smoothly and flow from point to point, *not* a laundry list.

INTRODUCTION

The Introduction establishes the context for your study, and answers questions such as:

- What relevant past work has been done by other researchers on your topic?
- Why is the topic interesting?
- Why is it important to the rest of biology or the world at large?
- What issues have not been resolved by other researchers?
- What issues are researchers still arguing about?
- What question does your study seek to answer?
- How are you going to answer that question?

A good Introduction usually includes the following components, generally in this order:

1. **A general context, providing background and importance.** If you're studying the effects of selection on genetic variation, briefly describe what relevant work has already been done. (See the note on avoiding plagiarism below.) Also indicate why knowledge about this topic is important. How does it relate to other issues or topics in biology?

2. **What is still unknown about your topic?** If everything was already known about your topic, there would be no need for you (the researcher) to do a study. Provide a context for your work by highlighting relevant controversies or weak spots in current knowledge. This portion of the Introduction often includes phrases like: "It remains unknown, however, ..." or "Previous work has failed to ..."

3. **A brief description of your system (e.g., the organisms or tools you are working with), and why it is appropriate for the questions you are addressing.** You may also want to briefly indicate the techniques you will be using. You will be describing your experiment in much greater detail in your Methods section; here you should only give as much detail as is necessary for someone unfamiliar with your experiment to understand the questions you are asking and the hypotheses/predictions you are making (#4, below).

4. **The specific questions/hypotheses you will address (these should relate closely to what you said was still unknown about your topic (#2, above)).** Don't be afraid to state it bluntly: "This study will address the following questions…" or "This study will test the hypothesis that…" Clarity is much more important than elegance of prose. Depending on the nature of the study, you might also indicate *how* your results will allow you to test the competing hypotheses or fill the gaps in knowledge that you described in #2. You should also state what results you expected before you did your experiment—these are your hypotheses or predictions.

Once you have consulted **primary resources**, you should have all the information you need to write the Introduction (although you may need to revise it later, i.e., in the Discussion).

Any attempt to pad the introduction with peripheral details will reduce the impact of this section. The goal is to supply enough information to clue the reader in to the purpose of the study and the general approach taken by the author. **Be careful not to plagiarize content from your textbook or other sources—use your own words and cite everything!** Remember, your goal is to *summarize* relevant findings from other sources, not quote specific ideas or results. In scientific writing, we rarely if ever quote from sources; you should *never* do so in your lab reports.

Check out the University's page about plagiarism:
http://www.lib.umd.edu/UES/plag_stud_what.html

METHODS
The methods section is often the easiest part to write, and is a good place to start if you're having "writer's block." Your methods section should contain enough detail for a reader unfamiliar with this experiment to repeat every aspect of the study. At the same time, there should not be so many details that the reader gets lost. Describe in prose—do not use bullets or recipe style writing. This section should be written in active voice.

"DOs" OF METHODS SECTION

1. Do report all important information. For example, the time spent in a water bath, the temperature of the bath, whether the bath was shaking, incubation times, how much chemical was used, the purpose of the chemicals, the concentration or other important information about the chemicals, etc.
2. Do explain the method of data collection. Were the data gathered individually or pooled with those of fellow researchers? Were samples chosen systematically, randomly, or haphazardly?
3. Include a brief description of data analysis and any statistical procedures that you used. Do not include formulas or descriptions of how to carry out the tests, just mention what tests you used to analyze your data.
4. Use complete sentences.
5. Remember to **cite your lab manual** as well as any other sources. You did not pull the procedures out of thin air!

"DON'TS" OF METHODS SECTION

1. Don't write this section as a cookbook. In other words, this section should not be written with a series of numbered steps.
2. **Don't simply rewrite the methods from your manual (that would be plagiarism).** This should be a *distilled* version of the methods.
3. Don't include common equipment in this section. If the instructions in your lab manual tell you to mix chemicals into a 25 ml beaker, they may do so because that is the best equipment available to the lab prep people. That does not mean that a 25 ml beaker is the only acceptable container in which to mix the chemicals. Therefore, in your methods section, simply state that the chemicals were mixed. You may assume that your reader has knowledge of common laboratory procedures and you need not discuss them in detail. Other common equipment does not need step-by-step instructions for use; it is adequate to simply state what equipment you used and what you used it for. Examples of this equipment include microscopes, spectrophotometers, balances, hemacytometers, and pipettors.

RESULTS

It's often helpful to make your figures (graphs, etc.) and tables before writing the Results section. The figures and tables should be chosen to illustrate points relevant to the questions you posed in the introduction, not to summarize all the data you collected. Don't include both tables and figures if the tables don't add any new information not shown in your figures. Do not include your raw data, unless you wish to use it as an illustration (when you wish to show raw data for some reason, they can be included in Appendices).

Once you've completed your figures and tables, writing the Results section amounts primarily to a simple description of them. Highlight important trends and statistical differences, as relevant to your questions, but do not interpret them. For example, "Oak leaves are significantly larger on the northern side of trees" is appropriate. However, continuing the sentence with "...because of lower light levels" is not appropriate. The first part of the sentence is a description of your findings; the second part is a statement about the implications, and belongs in your Discussion.

HOW TO REFER TO TABLES AND FIGURES

Every table and figure must be referred to in the text, in the order in which it is numbered. References to tables and figures should be in the following format:

"As light intensity increases, so does seedling growth rate (Fig. 1);"
or
"As light intensity increases, so does seedling growth rate (Table I)"

HOW TO REPORT STATISTICAL SIGNIFICANCE

All statistics should be reported in the text with their calculated values, degrees of freedom, and significance ("p-value") indicated, either parenthetically or as a table. For example:

"In our population of spotted newts, those with long legs showed significantly higher survival than those with short legs ($X^2=6.15$, df=1, $p<0.05$)."

If your results did not show a significant difference you can report them like this:

"In our population of spotted newts, those with long legs did not show significantly higher survival than those with short legs ($X^2=0.16$, df=1, NS)."

TABLES AND FIGURES

All Figures and Tables must be constructed on the computer. If you are working in a group, do NOT print out multiple copies of the same figure. **Each student must make his/her own.** Otherwise, we won't know whether you did the work of making the graph yourself or you are trying to get credit for work done by somebody else, which would constitute plagiarism!

FIGURES

You should present your data in figures (i.e., graphs, pictures) when appropriate. These will demonstrate the results summarized in the text with more detail, and provide the reader the opportunity to interpret the results for themselves. Figures must on be separate pages at the end of the lab report and are referred to in the text (e.g., "Fig. 1"). Each figure must be accompanied by a **legend** that describes the figure precisely. **A figure and its legend must be able to stand alone and still be understood by the reader.** Examples of figures with legends are given below.

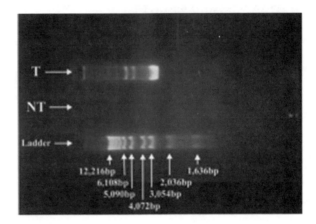

Figure 1. Agarose gel electrophoresis of pUC19 plasmid DNA isolated from cultured E. coli. NT, untransformed bacteria; T, transformed bacteria; Ladder, size standard (bp, base pairs). Gel = 0.8% agarose; buffer = 1X TBE.

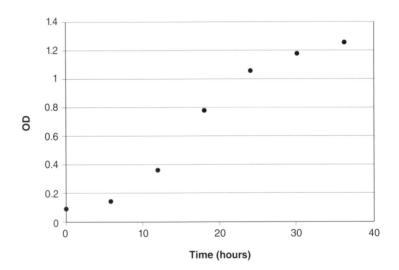

Figure 2. Optical density of pUC19 transformed E. coli.(strain DH5alpha) cultured in LB with ampicillin (100 µg/ml) as a function of time. Measurements were made at 600 nm.

TABLES

Data that are too complex or qualitative to make a figure are presented in tables numbered consecutively with Roman numerals and cited in the text (e.g., "Table II"). Each table is typed on a separate page and includes a title and explanatory notes. **Again, a table must be able to stand alone and still be understood by the reader.** Look at the example below and notice how additional information is provided as a note.

Table I. Effects of compounds on the incidence of plasmolysis and mortality of Saccharomyces cerevisiae *cells.*[a]

Number of Plasmolyzed Cells/Total Number of Cells Alive at Day					
Compound	4	6	8	10	12
Control	0/30	23/30	24/24	13/13	7/7
Hops Extract	0/10	0/10	0/10	1/10	4/10
Barley Extract	0/10	1/10	6/9	6/7	2/3
3B105	0/10	8/10	9/10	6/6	2/2
Ethanol	0/10	0/10	2/10	2/9	5/9

[a] Twenty-five-hour-old yeast cultures with a fresh weight of 16 to 18 mg were inoculated with the shown compounds and treated twice daily for 6 days. Plasmolysis was determined to be complete at 50% cell shrinkage.

NOTE: There is more information about how to construct appropriate Tables and Figures on the course Web site.

DISCUSSION

A good discussion explains the results in light of the hypothesis and other related work in the field. All of the data should be mentioned and related to the basic questions that were asked in the Introduction. Do not simply restate the information already presented in the Introduction. Interpretation and conjecture are permissible here, but only if they are clearly indicated as being the author's ideas.

In the Discussion you should briefly restate the central questions of your paper (as indicated in your Introduction), and the specific hypotheses that were tested. This brings the reader back to why the study was done in the first place, and focuses your Discussion on the relevant issues.

You should discuss how your findings relate to the questions you posed in the Introduction. If you asked two questions in your Introduction, make sure you address them both *specifically and individually*. If your data don't allow you to answer the questions definitively, say so, and indicate what additional information you would need to answer it.

You began your paper with a description of the general background and importance of the topic you investigated. Now you need to revisit that same information. How do your conclusions regarding your specific questions relate to that general context? How do your results compare with those obtained by the author(s) of your primary source(s)? If they are different, what explanations do you have for those differences? How do your results contribute to the general state of knowledge in the field?

Finally, you should discuss what questions remain—or what questions your results have raised—that warrant further investigation. NOTE: for this part of the discussion, don't just write out all the problems with your lab or state that you would do the same lab again. Think about what *new* experiments should be done, or what other questions you would want to ask if you did a follow-up study.

LITERATURE CITED

In your lab report, you ***must*** have references in two forms: a **Literature Cited** section at the end of the report, and **in text citations** throughout the report. The in text citations inform the reader where the ideas, background information and data not generated by you came from originally. This allows readers to look up the cited works for themselves, and allows them to double check your interpretation of the original source material. In addition, it is important to accurately attribute works to their original authors—they deserve credit for all of their hard work!

The final section of every lab report will be the **Literature Cited**, also known as the references. In the life sciences we typically call this section Literature Cited because, well, it lists the sources you actually cite in the text of the lab report. In some other disciplines, they might include general references or a bibliography of relevant papers even if they are not directly cited—we do not do that.

Any time you submit an article to be published, or a proposal for a research grant, you will be given a specific format for citing references. If you do not cite your references properly, your paper or grant proposal will be refused. On the following page, you are given guidelines on how to cite articles and format your works cited. This is often a format that students are not used to, but you need to make sure you follow it exactly to get full credit.

Helpful hint: keep the authors in the same order as they are listed on the paper or book. This is because authors are listed in order of contribution to the paper, so being first author is important. If the article or book has two authors put "and" between the names in both the literature cited and the text. If the article or book has more than two authors, list all of the authors in the literature cited, but just write the first author's last name, followed by "et al." and the year in the text.

Reference to the work of others is always acceptable when properly cited, but constitutes plagiarism otherwise. To cite literature within your text, place the citation at the end of the sentence in parentheses. The citation must include the author's last name and the year of publication.

One author example: Two predators can lead to a synergistic interaction (Losey 1996).
Two author example: Omnivory occurs in the mired family (Eubanks and Langellotto 1995).
Multiple author example: Planthoppers take 40 days to mature (Denno et al. 1997).
Multiple references: Surfperch give birth to live young (Agassiz 1854; Eigenmann 1887).

FORMATS FOR LITERATURE CITED

Journal Article
Author(s). Year. Title. *Journal title*. Volume: pages.

One author:
Scheffer, S.J. 2002. New host record, new range information, and a new pattern of voltinism: possible host races within the holly leafminer *Phytomyza glabricola* Kulp (Diptera: Agromyzidae). *Proceedings of the Entomological Society of Washington*. 104: 571–575.

For example, the holly leafminer has a univoltine lifecycle on one host, *Ilex coriacea*, but a multivoltine lifecycle on its other host, *I. glabra* (Scheffer 2002).

Two authors:
Fienberg, S.E. and Stern, P.C. 2006. In search of the magic lasso: The truth about the polygraph. *Statistical Science*. 20: 249–260.

Polygraph tests may not be as accurate as many people believe (Fienberg and Stern 2006).

Three or more authors:

Abrahamson, W.G., Eubanks, M.D., Blair, C.P., and Whipple, A.V. 2001. Gall flies, inquilines, and goldenrods: a model for host-race formation and sympatric speciation. *American Zoologist.* 41: 928–938.

Evidence suggests that sympatric speciation may be more prevalent than once thought (Abrahamson et al. 2001).

Article in Book

Author(s) of article. Year. Title of article. In: Editor(s) of book. *Title of book.* Publisher: City, pages.

Harrison, R.G. 1998. Linking evolutionary pattern and process: the relevance of species concepts for the study of speciation. In: Howard, D.J. and Berlocher, S.H. *Endless Forms: Species and speciation.* Oxford University Press: New York, 19–31.

Different species concepts fall at different points along the continuum between polymorphic populations and genealogical species (Harrison 1998).

Book

Author(s). Year. *Title.* Publisher: City.

Coyne, J.A. and Orr, H.A. 2004. *Speciation.* Sinauer Associates, Inc: Sunderland.

Evolutionary biologists have not yet decided on a single definition of a species (Coyne and Orr 2004).

Jensen, J.S. 2008. *Ecology and Evolution Lab Manual.* Hayden-McNeil Publishing: Plymouth, MI.

There are two main theories for the origin of humans: multiregional and replacement (Jensen 2008).

Keller, M.J. and Lanford, P.J. 2008. *Introduction to Experimental Biology.* Hayden-McNeil Publishing: Plymouth, MI.

A time-course was determined for production of *p*-nitrophenol by alkaline phosphatase using the following method (Keller 2008).

Freeman, S. 2005. *Biological Science.* 2nd ed. Pearson Prentice Hall: Upper Saddle River, N.J.

Insects have more species than any other form of life (Freeman 2005).

Web Site

In general, the use of Web sites as references is frowned upon. Scientific or scholarly publications have been through a stringent process of peer review, fact-checking and editing. That is why they are considered reliable sources of information. Web sites, on the other hand, span a range from reliable to purposefully misleading and do not have to meet any standards. For this reason, **Web sites will not be accepted as references** in your lab reports. **You should find the original source discussed on the Web site and use that as your reference.**

A FINAL WORD: EDITING

You can maximize your chance of getting the highest grade possible of the lab reports by following these simple rules:

- Always proofread the final draft. In fact, have another person proofread it as well, especially if English is not your first language or you are insecure about the quality of your writing. Try reading it out loud—if it sounds choppy or unclear when you hear it, it probably is (we tend to be more forgiving of writing, especially our own, as long as we can read it easily).

- Always spell-check the final draft.

- Double-check that everything is included before handing it in.

BSCI 105

Poster Presentation Guide

The **poster** is a common medium for communication within the scientific community. Posters are of particular value at scientific meetings where there tend to be large numbers of people and it is not practical for everyone to give a talk. Also, posters are often used to present incomplete studies and solicit feedback from fellow scientists before proceeding to publication.

Obviously, students in BSCI 105 cannot present original research, but we consider the experience of making and presenting a poster a valuable exercise. You will construct a poster that discusses a general topic of interest to you and focus on presenting one paper you consider especially relevant. You will accomplish this by addressing the following items, in order:

1. Introduction to your topic, with a discussion of general background and relevance to science and society.
2. Questions that still need be addressed relating to the topic.
3. A summary of one recent paper that addresses one of those questions. This will include presenting their goals and hypotheses, methods, results, and conclusions in your own words.
4. A discussion of how you see the focal paper fitting in with the larger issues discussed in Items 1 and 2.
5. Future directions: Where do you think the field of research on your topic is or should be heading to address remaining questions?

Teams

You must work in a team of two for this presentation. Part of this exercise is intended to foster your ability to work together. Still, if you have chronic problems with a partner, notify your TA immediately, so that the situation can be addressed.

Topic Selection

You should choose a topic related directly to the material covered in the course. This covers a lot of ground, so make sure it is a topic that is interesting to you. Posters should also include a *major new finding*. This new finding must come from a **primary source**—meaning, an original research article found through PubMed or a similar scientific literature database.

Overall Presentation

You should obtain a three-panel folded poster board that will stand up on its own on the lab tables. The title should be legible from at least several feet back, and the design of the poster should be straightforward and professional (not too "arts and crafty"). Make sure the typeface you use for the text is large enough to be read easily, and you do not overwhelm the poster with text. Likewise, figures should be large and clear, and your **original** figure legends complete and concise.

The format of the content should reflect the scientific journal-style presentation that we use for lab reports. (At real scientific conferences, the posters are formatted that way to make it very easy to go ahead and publish the information.)

Components

Title, Abstract, General/Specific Background, Methods, Results, Figures, Conclusions, Future Directions, and References.

COMPONENT DETAILS

The general structure and content of the sections of your poster will be similar to the parts of your lab reports. You can refer to the lab report instructions for guidance.

The title should be concise and inclusive.

The abstract should cover both general background and the specific background of the new finding. Also include a brief description of methodologies and results from the focal paper, and their relation to the broader topic.

The introduction/background should include the background that ties this topic to material presented in this course. *For example,* if you were doing a poster on sickle cell anemia, then you should include a brief background on point mutations and quaternary structure of hemoglobin. You would then move on to provide a background on the specific topic you are interested in. *In our sickle cell anemia example*, this might include a summary of the prevalence of this condition and what is currently known about its cause and treatment.

Finally, you would introduce the focal paper you have chosen with a summary of the relevance of those findings to the general topic.

Remember to include embedded citations in the body of your text!

The *methods* should be a brief (not too detailed) overview of the methods used in the new research you are presenting.

The *results* should summarize the major findings of the focal paper that are most relevant to your topic.

Figures should be large and clear, and you should definitely be able to explain them! Figure legends should be **original**, describing the content of the figure and emphasizing the results most relevant to your topic.

Conclusions should discuss the interpretation of the author's own results from the focal paper, as well as your interpretation as related to your topic.

Future directions should be about the same length as the abstract (i.e., one paragraph), and should include a discussion about unanswered questions and future research that might be helpful to this field.

Lastly, you should have at least four references, including a **minimum of two** journal articles from primary sources found in a database such as PubMed. The other two can be the textbook, the lab manual, or other reports and scientific books. All references listed at the end of the poster must be cited within the body of the text someplace.

PEER AND TA EVALUATION (35 POINTS TOTAL)

Your poster, and your presentation of it, will be assessed by all of the other teams in the lab, as well as the lab TA. Each individual team member will be asked to go over the poster, *by themselves*, and so each must know the information well. The specific items that will be evaluated include:

1. Choice of topic (relatedness to course material, level of interest)

2. Presenter's knowledge of information

3. Organization of presentation, format, logic

4. Presenter's handling of Q & A

5. Quality of visual aids

Basic Laboratory Equipment

The following five exercises are designed to familiarize you with common and essential laboratory equipment. Each of the exercises deals with a separate tool that is used frequently in modern biological laboratories. Since you will need to use these pieces of equipment correctly and accurately throughout the laboratory course, it is important that you learn their proper use here.

The Star Points placed throughout this manual provide information and questions that are intended to get you thinking. See how many you can answer!

B SCI 105

The Micropipettor

Many procedures used in modern biological research laboratories require the repeated, accurate measurement of very small volumes of liquid. The micropipettor is a sophisticated and delicate mechanical device for dispensing small volumes, typically less than one milliliter, and often as little as one microliter. This exercise will familiarize you with the operation and handling of the micropipettor.

Background

It is possible that you are unfamiliar or uncomfortable using the metric system of weights and measures. By the time you complete this exercise you must be able to confidently use and convert between metric units. All measurements used in science are made and reported in metric units (liters for volume, grams for weight, and meters for size). It is very important that everyone uses the same units of measurement in order to understand, execute, and repeat experiments.

CNN Headline, September 30, 1999:

"NASA's metric confusion caused Mars orbiter loss"

"NASA lost a $125 million Mars orbiter because one engineering team used metric units while another used English units…"

This exercise deals specifically with the measurement of **volume**, so you need to understand the relationships between liters, milliliters and microliters. Note the following relationships:

1 liter (L) is equal to a little more than a quart.

1 milliliter (ml) is 1/1,000th of a liter, or 10^{-3} L.
This volume is also known as a cc, for cubic centimeter. One ml of water takes up a cubic centimeter of volume and (incidentally) weighs one gram.

1 microliter (µl) is 1/1,000,000th of a liter, or 10^{-6} L.
This is a very small volume indeed: a very small drop. (Also note that 1 microliter is 1/1,000 of a milliliter, or 10^{-3} ml.) So, 1 L = 1×10^3 ml = 1×10^6 µl.

The volume measurements in this exercise (and throughout the course) are often given in terms of microliters, tens of microliters, or hundreds of microliters, rather than milliliters.

For example:

0.002 ml = 2 µl, 0.05 ml = 50 µl, 0.3 ml = 300 µl

The very tiny volume of 2 µl is at the lowest range of the micropipettor that we will use in this class. In practice, there are also micropipettors that can measure even smaller volumes, down to 0.25 µl.

See if you can make the following conversions:

0.45 ml = _____ µl
6.1 ml = _____ µl
0.033 ml = _____ µl

Understanding the Micropipettor Settings

The numerical display on the side of the micropipettor shows the volume than can be drawn. You will be required to read the setting of three types of micropipettors: the P-20, P-200, and the P-1000. These dispense at maximum volumes of 20 µl, 200 µl, and 1,000 µl, respectively. Examine the diagrams on the next page and compare them to the equipment on your bench. Your TA will help you interpret the display on each micropipettor so that you use the appropriate one for each volume you want to dispense. **It is *very* important that you learn to understand these settings**, since you will use this equipment to measure reagents throughout the course!

IMPORTANT: If you are not comfortable setting the micropipettor at any time during the semester, ask your TA for help! You should not have to force the dials, and attempting to go beyond the maximum range will break the micropipettor.

Diagram of Micropipettor

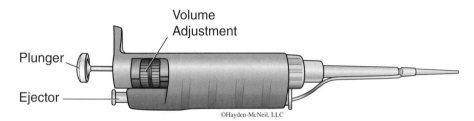

©Hayden-McNeil, LLC

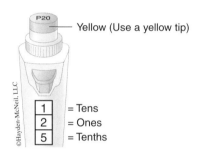

Yellow (Use a yellow tip)

1	= Tens
2	= Ones
5	= Tenths

Range = 2–20 μl
Set at: 12.5 μl

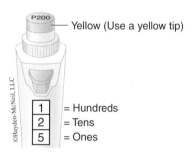

Yellow (Use a yellow tip)

1	= Hundreds
2	= Tens
5	= Ones

Range = 20–200 μl
Set at: 125 μl

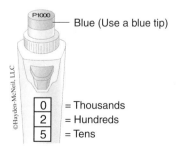

Blue (Use a blue tip)

0	= Thousands
2	= Hundreds
5	= Tens

Range = 200–1000 μl
Set at: 250 μl

Procedure

1. **Obtain from your TA:**

   Disposable blue plastic pipette tips (1,000 μl)
   Disposable yellow plastic pipette tips (200 μl)
   A graded microcentrifuge tube (return this small plastic tube to your TA at
      the end of class)
   P-20, P-200, P-1000 (There are a limited number of micropipettors, so the
      class will share)
   Two small samples of colored water
   A microcentrifuge tube rack

2. **Take a micropipettor that has a plunger labeled 1000 (dispenses up to
   1,000 μl, or 1 ml). There are several important things to notice about this
   device.**

   Locate the plunger. This button is depressed to displace a volume of air
   and then is released to draw up a volume of liquid. The plunger number
   (in this case 1000) denotes the maximum amount of liquid that can be
   obtained by this micropipettor.

   > **NEVER ATTEMPT TO OBTAIN MORE LIQUID THAN THE
   > MAXIMUM AMOUNT THE DEVICE IS CALIBRATED FOR!
   > NEVER TURN THE DIAL OUTSIDE ITS RANGE!**

   Notice that the plunger top is color coded to match the proper disposable
   micropipettor tips. The top of the P-1000 is blue; therefore, you would use
   blue tips. The bottom of the micropipettor must ALWAYS be covered with
   a disposable tip when drawing up any liquid!

   Locate the ejector button. This button is below the plunger on the side of
   the micropipettor. It will remove the disposable micropipettor tip.

3. **Put a disposable tip on your micropipettor.** Be sure that your tip is on
   securely. After practicing, you will notice that a secure tip fit is crucial and
   should be double-checked.

4. **Eject the tip using the ejector button.** Practice steps 2 and 3 until you are
   comfortable with the feel of the device.

5. **Now, practice drawing and dispensing 400 μl with the P-1000.** Examine
   the side of your micropipettor. You will notice that the window numbers read 040, showing that this particular micropipettor is set to draw

THE MICROPIPETTOR
....

BSCI 105

up 0.40 ml or 400 µl. (Study the figure in this manual until you have an understanding of how to read µl.) An important feature of a micropipettor is that the plunger has two "stops." The first stop you come to as you push down on the plunger will draw up the appropriate amount of liquid. The second stop is only used to dispense the final drop of your volume into an appropriate container. Your TA will demonstrate these stops for you.

a.   Firmly, put a blue tip on your micropipettor (but don't "ram" it on).

b.   Push down on the plunger until you are perfectly sure you know the difference between where the first stop is and where the second stop is.

c.   Push the plunger down to the **first stop**. Do not let the plunger up.

d.   Put the pipette tip into the yellow liquid so that no more than half of your blue disposable pipette tip is in the liquid.

e.   SLOWLY (*SLOWLY*) let the plunger up. The tip now contains 400 µl of liquid. Notice how much of the tip 400 µl takes up.

f.   Find your microcentrifuge tube and hold your micropipettor vertically so that the tip is in the tube, ready to dispense water.

g.   SLOWLY (*SLOWLY*) push the plunger to the first stop. DO NOT release the plunger. Continue to slowly push the plunger down to the second stop. Do not release the plunger yet! Withdraw the pipette tip from the liquid. Slowly let the plunger up.

Never lay a micropipettor down with the tip still on!

h.   Eject the tip and then return the micropipettor to the holder so that it is *upright*. This step is very important after each use. If liquid from the tip gets in the instrument (which won't happen if you pipette *SLOW-LY*), the instrument will be damaged. Never turn the micropipettor horizontally, even without a tip on, because condensation can build up and corrode the instrument.

6.   **Finally, now draw up 100 µl of blue liquid by using the P-200 (dispenses up to 200 µl).** Look at the tip after you draw the liquid and make note of how much of the yellow tip is filled when you draw 100 µl. Add the blue liquid to the microcentrifuge tube already containing your yellow solution.

What is the total quantity of green solution in your microcentrifuge tube? Check it against the graduation markings on the side of the tube.

Which micropipettor would you use to draw the following volumes of fluid?

0.98 ml
0.165 ml
0.30 ml

The Spectrophotometer

Use and Construction of a Standard Curve

One common task in the biology laboratory is to determine the concentration of a molecule such as DNA, RNA, or protein in solution. This can be easily accomplished using a spectrophotometer to measure the amount of light absorbed by a solution and comparing that to a standard curve defining the relationship between concentration and absorbance. This exercise will familiarize you with the operation of a spectrophotometer and the construction of a standard curve using solutions of known concentration.

Background

The white light you see, say from a bulb or the sun, is a compilation of all colors of light. When white light moves through a prism, the colors are separated. Each color corresponds to a wavelength range.

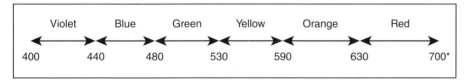

*Note that these wavelength ranges are approximate.

Based on this chart, what color would light of 425 nm appear? What color would light of 625 nm appear?

Molecules in solution absorb some wavelengths of light and transmit others. We see a solution as having a particular color when one wavelength is transmitted a lot better than other wavelengths. A solution appears blue, for example, because light in the range of 440–480 nm is transmitted while light of longer wavelengths is absorbed.

Consider a simple, although unrealistic, case where one color of light is always transmitted and all others color are entirely absorbed:

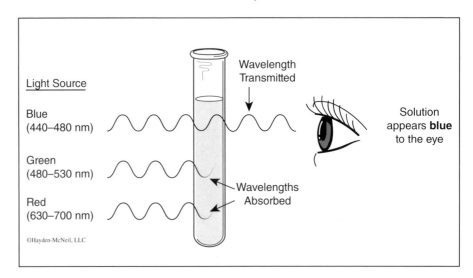

 Why does a green solution (such as the colored water in the pipettemen exercise) appear green? Complete the figure below to demonstrate which colors are absorbed by the solution and which are transmitted through the solution.

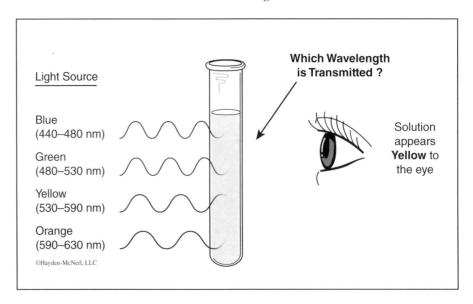

In most real solutions the different wavelengths of light are only partially absorbed, with some wavelengths being absorbed more than others. As the concentration of the molecule(s) in a solution increases the amount of light absorbed goes up proportionately. As a result, the relative amount of light at the transmitted wavelengths that reaches our eye increases and so does the intensity of the corresponding color.

A spectrophotometer is an instrument that directs light of a specific wavelength (i.e., color of light) through a solution (see figure below). Depending on the composition of the solution, a certain amount of that light will be absorbed by the solution, and a certain amount will pass through. The spectrophotometer contains a light-sensitive photocell that measures the amount of light that passes through the solution.

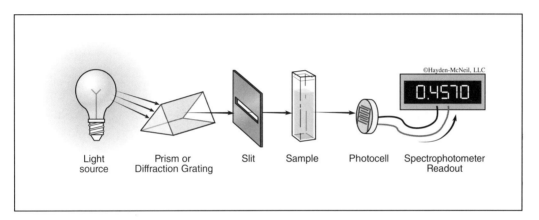

The spectrophotometer is used to quantify the amount of light passing through a solution. Two different types of units can be used. **Transmittance** is a measure of the percentage of light which passes through the solution. Conversely, the instrument may also be set to measure the amount of light absorbed by the solution. **Absorbance** is measured in optical density units or **OD**, which range in value from 0 to 1.999 OD units.

The relationship between transmittance and absorbance is expressed as:

$$A = \log_{10} \frac{1}{T}$$

where A = absorbance in OD units and T = transmittance.

For example, if the %T is 10% or 0.1, then A = log 1/0.1 = 1. (Relax! No need to do the mathematics. The spectrophotometer automatically displays the results in whatever units you desire.)

If a sample exhibits a high % transmittance at a particular wavelength, what can you infer about its absorbance at that wavelength?

One function of a spectrophotometer is to quantify the amount or concentration of a substance dissolved in a solution. Each substance in solution absorbs light of specific wavelengths. Thus, a blue solution absorbs wavelengths other than blue. The blue light passes through the solution and the solution is perceived by us as blue. A graph of the absorbance of different wavelengths of light by a specific substance is called an **absorption spectrum.**

*If a liquid is red, what wavelengths of light are **not** absorbed by the sample?*

*What wavelengths **are** absorbed?*

If a substance absorbs light of a specific wavelength, then the amount of the absorbed light is directly proportional to the concentration of the substance in solution.

This relationship is expressed as **Beer's law:**

OD = ec*l*

Where:
OD = absorbance (in optical density units)
e = extinction coefficient (the slope of the line resulting from a plot of **OD** vs. **c**)
c = concentration of the absorbing substance
l = length of the light path*
*Your spectrophotometer has a constant length light path of 1.0 cm.

At a fixed wavelength, a plot of the absorbance (in OD units on the y-axis) vs. the concentration (on the x-axis) results in a straight line with a slope of e. After constructing this plot (called a **standard curve**), it is a simple matter to determine the concentration of a substance by measuring its absorbance (OD). The graph below demonstrates this relationship.

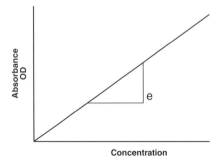

According to Beer's law, what is the relationship between the concentration of a substance and its absorbance?

Procedure: Operation of the Spectrophotometer

(Your TA should have instructed you to turn on the instrument. The machine needs a 30-minute warm-up period.)

BSCI 105

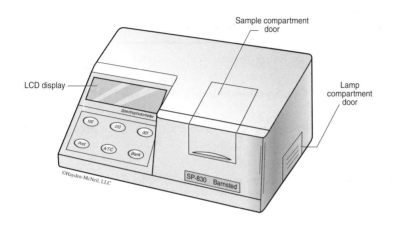

1. **Obtain 4 cuvettes.** A cuvette is an optically clear test tube or chamber that is designed to be used exclusively in the spectrophotometer. They look like small test tubes with special markings at the top. They are **not** test tubes and should be used only in the spectrophotometer.

2. **Into the first cuvette, dispense 8 [4] milliliters (ml) of water (H_2O) from Repipette 1.** The Repipette is set to dispense 2 milliliters of water per use. (Pump 4 times.) Write Tube #1 – 0 M at the top of the tube.

3. **To the second cuvette, dispense 6 [3] ml H_2O from Repipette 1 and add 2 [1] ml of colored solution from Repipette 2.** Label this tube #2 – 0.25 M.

4. **To the third cuvette, dispense 4 [2] ml H_2O from Repipette 1 and add 4 [2] ml of colored solution from Repipette 2.** Label this tube #3 – 0.50 M.

5. **To the fourth cuvette, dispense 2 [1] ml H_2O from Repipette 1 and add 6 [3] ml of colored solution from Repipette 2.** Label this tube #4 – 0.75 M.

 What is the difference between a cuvette and a test tube?

6. **Remove any cuvette** from the spectrophotometer and close the lid on the cuvette chamber.

Set the wavelength to 450 using the 100 and 010 buttons on the keypad.

Set the mode to absorbance by pressing the A/T/C button.

Insert cuvette containing "blank" solution and close the lid.

Press "BLANK" and wait until the display reads "0.000A."

Press "A/T/C" to confirm 100% Transmittance, then press twice more to return to absorbance.

Remove the blank and insert your first sample. Close the lid and wait for a stable reading.

 Which solution transmits more yellow light to your eye? If a yellow solution transmits yellow light, what colors (wavelengths) does it absorb? Check your answers with your TA before proceeding. Solution 4, absorbs all other wavelengths

Use the spectrophotometer to read the rest of your samples and fill in the data table below.

Construct a standard curve on the worksheet provided. Remember, a standard curve should always start at (0,0).

Each time you change the wavelength you must re-blank the machine, but not between samples at a single wavelength.

Table I. _____

Sample #	Absorbance (OD)	
	450 nm (blue)	550 nm (yellow)
1 (0%)	-0.159	-0.116
2 (25%)	0.038	-0.106
3 (50%)	0.297	-0.108
4 (75%)	0.463	-0.106

7. **Explain your results using Beer's law.** Remember, l is constant and equals 1.0 cm for the spectrophotometers. Calculate **e** based on your standard curve. (Remember, **e** is equal to the slope of the line of best fit—do not calculate it from your raw data points!)

8. **Change the wavelength to 550 nm. Read the absorbance at this setting.** What color is light of 550 nm? Should your yellow solutions absorb much of this light? Why? Test your guess to see if you are correct. (Should you use tube #1 to blank the machine?) Record your observations in the space provided in Table I.

   Which wavelength (450 nm or 550 nm) gave you the best indication of which solution contained the most yellow color? How do your data justify your answer?

   *What is the relationship between the display number (OD reading) and the wavelength you are beaming at your sample? **Think!** This is very important for later experiments!*

9. **Empty the cuvettes into the waste beaker.** Rinse the cuvettes with regular tap water. Do not use a test tube brush as it will scratch the glass. Rinse the cuvettes a final time with distilled water (in the plastic squeeze bottles by the sink) Return cuvettes to the rack at your bench.

BSCI 105

The Compound Microscope

BSCI 105

Background

Microscopes are designed to accomplish two tasks. First, they enlarge, or magnify, small objects. However, if an instrument enlarges an object, but the object remains fuzzy and unclear, the magnification is not very useful. (For example, you can sit very close up to the television set and still not be able to see the image any clearer than if you were back a few feet.) Consequently, the second task that microscopes are designed to accomplish is to provide increased **resolution** which is a function of the **resolving power** of the microscope. Resolving power is the ability to see two neighboring objects as distinct, separate entities. As resolving power increases, we are able to distinguish two points that are closer and closer together.

The construction of the microscope is specifically geared toward achieving these two tasks. The compound microscope consists of two types of lenses. One lens type, the **objective**, is placed close to the specimen and magnifies it with increased resolution. The second lens, the **ocular**, is placed near the eye and further enlarges the image. The total magnification is equal to the magnification of the objective lens ($10\times$, $20\times$, $40\times$, $100\times$) times the magnification of the ocular lens (usually $10\times$).

The resolution (R) of a microscope is determined by the wavelength of light passing through the microscope (λ), which is measured in nanometers (nm) of light, and the numerical aperture (**NA**), which is a unitless expression of the light-gathering abilities of the lens. The NA of a given objective lens is normally inscribed on the outside of the lens and ranges from 0.25 to 1.4.

$$R = \lambda/NA$$

The value that results from this equation is given in nm and represents **the distance that can be resolved between two points.** As the numerical value of the resolution decreases, the resolving power increases. In other words, a lens with high resolving power allows you to see objects that are very close together (**R,** in nm).

Choose differing wavelengths of light. (Remember the chart in the section on spectrophotometers?) Using 0.5 as the NA, what would the resolution be for each of the wavelengths?

What do you notice about the relationship between the wavelength of light and the resolution?

Procedure: Introduction to the Microscope

1. **Anatomy of the microscope.** Examine the microscope in front of you. See if you can identify all of the parts indicated on the diagram below.

The Compound Microscope

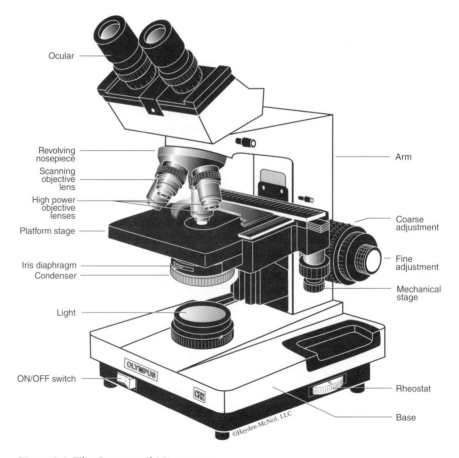

Figure 3.1. The Compound Microscope

2. **Storage of the microscope.** Compound microscopes are delicate instruments that are easily damaged through careless handling and improper storage. Note the following important points about how the microscope is left when not in use and ready to be put away.

- The power cord is loosely folded and tucked under the stage. Never wrap the cord tightly around the microscope base or arm as it will fatigue and break.

- The lowest power (scanning) objective is left in position. Never leave higher magnification objectives in place as they can crash into the condenser and break.

- There is no slide left on the stage.

3. **Handling of the microscope.** When moving the microscope, never slide it across the bench top—the rubber feet will cause vibrations that can harm the microscope optics. Always hold the microscope by the arm above the stage and support it by the base with your other hand. Never try to pick up a microscope by the stage! Lift the scope up and gently put it down to move it.

4. **Cleaning the microscope.** Under normal use there should be no need to clean the microscopes very often. If the stage gets wet from a slide, you can wipe it dry with a towel or Kimwipe. If you suspect your oculars are dirty, you may wipe them GENTLY with a LENS PAPER (no towels, Kimwipes or shirt sleeves, please!). If necessary the oculars can be wetted by breathing on them or a drop of isopropanol can by applied to the lens paper. Ask your TA for assistance before cleaning the oculars, please.

Never clean the objectives yourself—always ask your TA for assistance.

Procedure: Basic Use of the Microscope

It is the student's responsibility to handle the microscope carefully, and to see that it is cleaned and turned off after each use. Don't forget to remove the slide too!

> **MICROSCOPES ARE EXPENSIVE, SENSITIVE**
> **LABORATORY TOOLS. TREAT THEM GENTLY.**

1. **Place the microscope so that the stage and the oculars are facing you.** Unfold the power cord and plug in the microscope.

2. **Obtain a microscope slide** that has the letter "e" on it. You should find this slide in the microscope slide box labeled "microscope lab."

3. **Now place the slide on the microscope.** Open the spring-loaded clip on the stage (platform) of the microscope and insert the slide. Gently release the clip so that it rests against the slide (not on top of it).

4. **Set the position of the substage condenser.** Make sure the condenser lens is at a position just below the bottom of the slide. The condenser position can be adjusted up and down by the knob below the stage. The condenser lens focuses the light onto the object on the slide and must be in the correct position.

5. **Turn on the power switch.** Make sure the voltage dial on the side of the scope is at its highest setting, otherwise the light will have an orange color instead of white. Light intensity should be adjusted using the **iris diaphragm** under the condenser lens.

6. **Locate the objective lenses,** which are attached to a revolving nosepiece (turret). These objective lenses magnify the image of the specimen on the slide (see Figure 3.1).

There is a number written on the side of the lens that tells you the magnification value of that lens. These range from 4× to, in some cases, 100×. That is, the 4× lens magnifies the image four times. What other number have we discussed that is important in understanding the function of a given objective lens?

7. **If the 4× objective is not in position above the slide, turn the nosepiece** until it clicks into place.

8. **At this point, you will need to make some adjustments to the oculars (eyepieces) to be sure the microscope is set to your needs.** The oculars magnify the image by 10 times (they are 10×) and are placed on a sliding device that allows you to adjust the distance between the eyepieces. This distance is called the **interpupillary distance** and it differs for everyone. To find your proper setting, look through both eyepieces. Your eyes should be about one inch or so from the oculars. As you look through the oculars, slide the oculars inward or outward until the image you see resolves into one circle. This may take you a few minutes. The circle you see when looking through the oculars is called the **field of view.**

9. **If you have trouble achieving the single circle image** try varying the distance between your eyes and the oculars, which is often one source of the problem. If this does not help, you probably need to adjust the focus of the oculars themselves (see Figure 3.1). If you still have problems, consult with your TA.

10. **Using the stage controls located to the lower right side of the stage, move the specimen holder until the letter "e" is positioned over the condenser.** Look from the side of the microscope to determine when the letter "e" is over the condenser.

11. **To focus on the slide you will use the coarse and fine adjustment knobs.** These knobs are attached to the arm of the microscope on the right side. The large, inner knob is the coarse adjustment and you use it to bring the specimen into a basic focus. The small, outer knob is the fine adjustment and it is used to bring the specimen into clear focus. Your TA will instruct you on how to bring the specimen into focus.

> **ONLY USE THE COURSE FOCUS WITH THE 4× SCANNING LENS. NEVER USE COURSE FOCUS WITH THE HIGHER MAGNIFICATION LENSES IN PLACE!**

12. **Adjust the oculars for differences between your left and right eyes.** Bring the letter "e" into sharp focus using just your right eye. Turn the adjustment ring on the left ocular until both eyes see the image in equally sharp focus. Start with the adjustment ring on "0."

13. **Move the specimen holder so that some portion of the letter "e" is in the center of your field of view.** This is important because it will help you find the specimen as you increase and decrease the magnification.

What is the total magnification of the letter "e" at this point? (Remember that both the objective and the ocular provide magnifying power.)

14. **The microscope you are using is a parfocal microscope;** when the specimen is in focus at one magnification, it will be largely in focus at another magnification. To test this concept, turn the objective nosepiece to the low power objective. DO NOT move the stage. The image should still be in fairly clear focus. To bring the image into sharp focus, adjust the **fine** adjustment knob. Spend a few minutes gaining familiarity with the stage controls by moving the stage so that you view all parts of the slide.

Why is it important to center the image before you increase magnification?

When you move the stage, does the image move in the same direction? Why?

15. **Observe the orientation of the letter "e."** Make sure you have the letter "e" slide with the label on the left so that the "e" is properly oriented on the slide. Observe the letter "e" as you see it through the microscope oculars and sketch it on the worksheet (page 27). How would you describe the orientation of the letter "e" as viewed through the compound microscope?

16. **Practice moving the slide using the mechanical stage.** There are two knobs mounted vertically below the stage. While looking at the stage, move the knobs and observe how the stage moves left-to-right or forward-and-backward. Remember which way you need to turn the knobs to make the slide move toward you and to the left. Look through the oculars and turn the knobs in the same way; how does the image of the letter "e" move?

Procedure: Preparation of a Wet Mount I

A wet mount is a method of preparing a slide that will be used for only a few minutes or hours. Unlike the letter "e" slide, which had the letter permanently mounted under a glass coverslip, a wet mount is made by placing a loose coverslip over a drop of water containing the specimen to be viewed.

1. **Locate the beaker that contains branches of the aquatic plant, *Elodea*.** Notice that the leaves of this plant are quite thin (only two cell layers thick!).

2. **Using forceps, carefully remove a leaf from the plant.** Place the leaf or part of the leaf onto a clean microscope slide. Using a plastic transfer pipette (dropper) place a drop of water on the leaf—**a small drop will suffice.** Get a coverslip and place the coverslip at a 45° angle over the slide. (See the figure below right.) Gently lower the coverslip over the *Elodea* leaf. Lowering the coverslip in this manner helps to eliminate air bubbles from under the coverslip.

3. **On the worksheet sketch one or two plant cells and label:** cell wall, cytoplasm, and chloroplasts, which you should be able to see moving within the cells. This is not the time to be Leonardo da Vinci! Draw for scientific accuracy. These specimens may also be viewed under phase contrast (see next section).

(a)

(b)

(c)

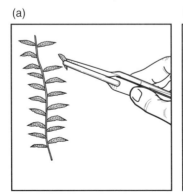
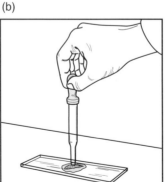
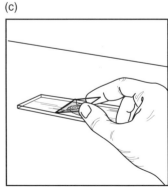

Procedure: Preparation of a Wet Mount II

Some cellular material has no pigmentation or coloring of any kind and must be viewed with special microscope settings. An example of this might be cell cultures in a laboratory, which cannot be stained with dyes and mounted permanently without destroying the cells. We use **phase contrast microscopy** to visualize this type of cellular material. Below, this type of microscopy is demonstrated through the use of cheek cells from the inside lining of your mouth.

Two special parts are needed for phase contrast microscopy: a substage phase contrast condenser turret (already on the microscope), and phase contrast objectives (the low and high power objectives on the microscope are phase contrast).

1. **Gently scrape the inside lining of your cheek with a clean toothpick.** Rub the toothpick on the slide to make a smear of cells. Mount a coverslip on top of the smear as you did previously. Place the slide on the microscope and notice that, with regular "brightfield" microscopy, these cells are very difficult to see.

2. **Place your cheek cell slide** so that the area containing cells is over the condenser. Move the turret of the condenser to the 10 position and move the 10× objective into place. To find the cheek cells move the stage to the highest point and then slowly move the coarse adjustment knob until the slide comes into focus. Use the fine focus knob to obtain clear resolution. You may need to increase the light if the field of view is too dark. Try placing a color filter over the light source. Does that improve the image?

3. Change to the 40× objective and move the condenser ring to the 40 position to observe one or more cheek cells at a higher magnification. **Draw what you see** on the worksheet.

Troubleshooting the Compound Microscope
PROBLEM: FIELD IS DARK (INSUFFICIENT LIGHT)

1. Power switch on base is not on.

2. The voltage control dial is too low. Turn dial higher.

3. The objective has not clicked into place. Turn nosepiece until objective clicks into place.

4. The condenser turret is not on "0" for brightfield microscopy, "10" for 10× phase contrast, or "40" for 40× phase contrast. Turn turret to appropriate setting.

5. The condenser is not raised to the highest setting, closest to the stage. Move condenser up.

6. The iris diaphragm is closed. Open diaphragm.

PROBLEM: IMAGE IS BLURRED

1. Dirty objective or slide. Clean first with lens paper. Ask instructor for assistance with cleaning fluid if objective does not clear after wiping.

2. Focus is incorrect. Use coarse adjustment on 4× to focus up or down. Image should move if slide is moved.

3. **If the image does not move** when you move the stage, you are not focused on the slide. To find the proper image, move the turret to the 4× objective and move the stage to the highest position with the coarse adjustment knob (large, inside knob). Then, looking through the eyepieces SLOWLY move the stage down until you get an image that is more or less in focus. Using the coarse adjustment, get the image fairly clear, then use the fine adjustment (small, outer knob) to bring the image into clear focus.

4. Too much light. Use the condenser diaphragm to limit the amount of light passing through the slide.

Resources on the Web and UMD Libraries Research Port

Background

Recent years have seen an explosion of resources on the internet (aka "the Web") that have transformed the way molecular biologists work. At the heart of this revolution in information technology has been the concept of free and open access to information. The volume and ease of access to shared information on the Web has greatly accelerated the pace of scientific discovery.

Publicly available internet resources include literature databases, genome databases, data repositories, protein model databases, and open source software repositories to name a few. Many of these are easily accessible through **NCBI**, the National Center for Biotechnology Information (http://www.ncbi.nlm.nih. gov/). In the following exercises you will be using PubMed, Online Mendelian Inheritance in Man, and Bookshelf through the NCBI Web site.

In addition to the publicly available resources, most universities subscribe to various databases and journals and make them freely available to all students. The University of Maryland Libraries provide a common access point to many such resources through **Research Port** (http://researchport.umd.edu/). This exercise will give you a brief introduction to Web of Science, online journals, and interlibrary loan.

"THE TRUT' IS OUT THERE"; SO ARE THE LIES

The Worl' *N*ide Web is an amazing resource and powerful tool, but it should always ʾ used with a healthy degree of caution and skepticism. The resources introdᵈ ed in this exercise are built upon a solid scientific foundation and proᵛ ᵉ access largely to **primary sources** and **peer-reviewed literature**. These reˑ ᵣces can be used with a significant degree of trust that the information ˑ ᵉnted is objective and reliable.

Many sites on the Web are designed for a subjective purpose and promote a particular agenda. It is often difficult to judge the degree to which information presented on the Web has been filtered, distorted or outright made-up. It is perfectly acceptable to go to Wikipedia or *Men's Health* magazine for information on an unfamiliar topic, but these are not primary sources. Any information presented in encyclopedias or journalistic media needs to be traced back to its original (primary) source, validated, and cited directly.

SEARCHING DATABASES

The most difficult part of searching resources on the internet is choosing the right **keywords**. Think about the most unique and important words that specifically describe the information you want to search for. Many search engines use **Boolean operators** to conduct searches with more than one keyword. The most useful of these are AND (must include all keywords), OR (must include at least one of the keywords), and NOT (must include the first keyword but not the second). An exact phrase can also be searched for by putting a string of words in quotes (" ").

Procedure I: Finding Papers in PubMed

PubMed is a freely accessible public database of scientific literature hosted by NCBI. PubMed contains the same information as the pay-for-use MedLine (available through Research Port) but lacks a sophisticated search engine. PubMed includes journals relevant to medical science in particular and is not a good place to find information on more agricultural or ecological topics, for example.

1. **Access the NCBI Web site.** Point your Web browser to http://www.ncbi. nlm.nih.gov/.

2. **Select "PubMed" from the search menu near the top of the page and enter the name of the researcher provided by your TA.** PubMed, like many literature databases, accepts author names as *Last Name* (space) *Initials*. So to search for Elaine Fuchs, for example, one would enter *Fuchs E* in the search box. Including a middle initial may narrow results further, especially with common surnames.

3. **Click on the "GO" button to execute your search.** A list of publications that include the author you searched for will be given in reverse chronological order. If there are a lot of papers, they will be displayed on multiple pages; you will have to use the "NEXT" button to see more.

4. **Click on the first article author list.** This will take you the abstract for the article. A link to the publisher Web site will be displayed in the upper right of the article record if the library has a subscription to the journal. Click on that link and you will have access to the full-text article. If you are off campus, you may need to look up the article through Research Port (below).

 How many articles did your search find? __850__

5. **Enter the author name in combination with a keyword provided by your TA.** This will narrow your results to papers by the author relevant to your topic of interest. For example, to search for papers by Elaine Fuchs having to do with skin, one would enter *Fuchs E skin* in the search box.

 How many articles did your search find? __196__

6. **Narrow your search to only include review articles.** Click on the "Review" tab at the top of the article list. Review articles summarize what is known about a topic and may or may not include original data. Review papers usually do have original ideas or models, however, and can be considered primary literature.

 How many articles did your search find? __36__

Procedure II: Researching Heritable Diseases in Man

Online Mendelian Inheritance in Man (OMIM) is a searchable database of heritable human diseases and syndromes for which there is information about the underlying genetic defect.

1. **Go to the NCBI home page.**

2. **Select "OMIM" from the search menu and enter *pituitary adenoma* (or your affliction of choice) into the search box and click "GO."**

3. **Click on the ID number of the first entry.** This takes you to the database record for that disease or syndrome. This page provides a summary of information known about the condition including:

- **Gene Map Locus**—the chromosomal location(s) of the associated gene(s)
- **Description**—the definition of the condition
- **Clinical Features**—symptoms observed in individuals diagnosed with the condition
- **Mapping**—data from which the chromosomal locations are inferred
- **Molecular Genetics**—information on candidate genes for the condition

4. **In the header of the record, find the menu labeled "Display."** Select "Gene links" from the menu—this will take you to a list of implicated genes for the condition that you can follow to further research individual genes.

Procedure III: Using the NCBI Electronic Bookshelf

NCBI is a division of the National Library of Medicine (NLM) and as such provides access to electronic versions of certain printed materials of significance to biomedical research.

1. **Go to the NCBI home page and select "BOOKS" from the blue banner at the top of the page.** This will take you to the NCBI electronic bookshelf. (Note that you can jump to other resources, including PubMed and OMIM, in the same way.)

2. **Browse the titles of the books.** You will see that the list includes a variety of publications such as textbooks, reports, methodological guides, and general references.

3. **Scroll down and click on the link for "The Cell—A molecular approach."** The table of contents will be displayed for the book, with a search box in the upper right of the page. From there you can search the full text of the book!

4. **Search for the keyword _Cyclin_.** You will get a list of all of the sections of the book containing the word "cyclin." Click on one of the links and you will get the full text of that section of the book, with links to figures.

Procedure IV: Research Port: Web of Science

One of the most powerful databases available through Research Port is **Web of Science**. Not only does the site have a more robust search engine and a wider variety of sources than PubMed, but Web of Science allows for **cited reference** searches. That means for any paper of interest, you can ask what other papers have used it as a reference!

1. **Go to Research Port at http://researchport.umd.edu/.** Note that access to Research Port from off campus will require you to log in.

2. **Under the "Databases" tab, go down to "by database name" and select "W."** This will take you to a list of all databases beginning with the letter W.

3. **Scroll down and select "Web of Science."** This will take you to the ISI Web site that hosts Web of Science, which is a subscription service.

4. **Search for the same author that you used in Procedure I (PubMed).** Make sure the "in" menu is set to "Author." Limit your search to the science database by unchecking the sociology and humanities databases under "Citation Databases."

How many results did you get? ~~1141~~ 1075

How does that compare with PubMed? Much More

5. **Try combining the author and topic searches just as you did in Procedure I.** Go back to the search page and enter the subject keyword in the second search box. Set the "in" menu for the second box to "Topic."

6. **Browse the results and find a reference that lists "Cited by" as greater than 0.** Click on the author list for that paper to go to the abstract page. The box on the right lists the references for papers that cite the one you selected. You can click on those links to go to those papers next.

7. **Click on the "Find it" button to see where the full text of the article is available.**

Procedure V: Research Port: Electronic Journals

Research Port also provides a central list of all journals to which the UMD Libraries subscribe that provide electronic access. In some cases access is limited to a few recent years, in others it stretches back decades. Do not be surprised if journals with paper subscriptions block access to the most recent 12 months online. This is irritating and inconvenient, but keeps them in business.

Nemto logica

1. **Go to the Research Port Web page and select the "Journals" tab.**

2. **Search for the journal suggested by your TA in the "journal name" box.** The results will list all journals with the search term(s) in their title and indicate available electronic access.

3. **Select a link to go to the journal Web site.** There will be a list of all electronically available volumes. From there you can read or download an article of interest from PubMed or other database.

Procedure VI: Interlibrary Loan

It is not unusual to find an article that is not available through electronic access or in paper form on the library shelves. What do you do then? You can request virtually any printed material, such as a book or journal article, through the **interlibrary loan** service.

1. **Go to the Research Port Web site.** Look for a box labeled "Looking for a specific article?"

2. **Enter as much information as you can about an article you would like to get.** For now, enter *Cytogenetics* and select "Find article."

3. **Click the "GO" button next to "Interlibrary Loan (ILL)."** You will be asked to log in to the ILL system using your UMD ID number. Once logged in you will be able to request materials.

4. **Alternatively, you can log into the ILL system directly through** http://www. lib.umd.edu/ILL/Welcome.html.

The resources presented here are but a sampling of the various tools available through the internet. The NCBI Web site alone provides access to many more different tools beyond those introduced today, including **Genbank** and **BLAST**, which you will explore later in the semester.

The Laboratory Notebook

If asked to name the most important tool commonly used by researchers in the life sciences, what would you choose? The microscope? The spectrophotometer? Perhaps even the computer? Certainly, each of these, and numerous others, have contributed significantly to the progress of different fields of biological research. However, there is a single item common to *all* fields of research that should top the list: the laboratory notebook.

The laboratory notebook is the principal record of every aspect of any properly conducted research study. It contains a summary of initial observations preceding any experiments and keeps track of hypotheses being tested, proposed experiments, detailed protocols, results, and initial interpretations of the data. The notebook provides a means of organizing thoughts and data so that even large and complex projects remain manageable. In today's world of patents and high-profit biotechnology, the laboratory notebook is also a valuable legal document that establishes a record of who-did-what-when. This is why we always use sewn-bound notebooks with permanent pages that cannot be removed.

COMPONENTS OF THE LABORATORY NOTEBOOK

The laboratory notebook includes the following types of information:

- Questions being addressed
- Initial observations
- Hypothesis or hypotheses, sometimes including a **null hypothesis**
- Summary and rationale of procedures to test each hypothesis
- Predictions about outcomes of experiments if a hypothesis is true
- An **exact** protocol for each procedure
- Results
- Initial interpretation of results
- Ideas about what to do next

ORGANIZATION OF THE LABORATORY NOTEBOOK

Typically, when starting a new notebook the first 3–4 pages are left blank and used to build an **index** of the laboratory notebook. All pages in the notebook are **numbered** consecutively so they can be referenced in the index. The index includes any categories considered relevant and need to be easy to look up at a later date, such as "Project Summaries," "Hypotheses," or "SDS-PAGE Gels." Page numbers are also used within the notebook to refer to earlier protocols or data when recording a new experiment.

Every page in a well-kept notebook has a **date** written above the first entry of each day on each page. That way, there is a record of when each part of an experiment was performed.

Procedure I: Pre-Lab Notes, Exercise 7

Starting next week, you will be required to keep a laboratory notebook with entries for each exercise that includes **pre-lab notes**, a **record of exact protocols**, **data**, and **interpretation of results**. The pre-lab notes need to be completed before each lab and will be checked by your TA. During lab, you should write out every step of the procedure **exactly** as it is performed, record your results, sketch any graphs, and record your preliminary interpretations and conclusions in consultation with your group.

1. **Starting on the third page of your composition notebook, enter today's date.**

2. **Label a new section "Background."** Read the scenario and background material for Exercise 7. Summarize these in your notebook, listing initial observations, what the problem is and what we already know.

3. **Label a new section "Hypotheses."** As a group, come up with one or more clear, precise hypotheses that you think Exercise 7 is designed to test. Since we have not yet discussed what a hypothesis is in any detail yet (that is part of Exercise 7), for now read the procedures and write out the questions you think they are designed to answer from the scenario and background material.

4. **Label a new section "Procedures."** In a few sentences, list the procedures to be used and a brief description of how they work and what they do. Detailed protocols will be added to this section as you perform the procedures next week.

5. **Have your TA initial your pre-lab notebook at the beginning of every lab.** The pre-lab notebook is **required** to be complete at the start of lab every week.

Procedure II: In-Lab Record Keeping, Exercise 7

During next week's lab, you will complete your notebook entries for Exercise 7.

1. **Write the date in your notebook before adding to it.**

2. **As a class, develop and agree upon final hypotheses for Exercise 7.** Record these in a new section labeled "Updated Hypotheses."

3. **Complete the "Procedures" section.** As a group, decide **exactly** what you will be doing for every step in Exercise 7. Write out an exact step-by-step protocol for each procedure, including specific volumes, times, etc., where appropriate.

4. **Label a new section "Results" and record all of your data as you perform the procedures.** Model tables and figures are provided in your lab manual. You can copy those in your notebook or create new ones if you have a better idea about organizing your data. You can use the graph paper in the lab manual to help make graphs and then sketch them in the lab notebook.

> **ALTHOUGH THIS MAY SEEM MORE THAN A LITTLE REDUNDANT BE-TWEEN THE LAB MANUAL AND THE NOTEBOOK, REMEMBER THAT THE POINT OF HAVING A WELL-KEPT LABORATORY NOTEBOOK IS THAT IT PROVIDES A *PERMANENT, UNALTERABLE* RECORD OF YOUR DATA. YOUR LAB MANUAL CAN BE TAKEN APART AND PUT BACK TOGETHER, AND PAGES CAN BE REMOVED WITHOUT ANY OBVIOUS EVIDENCE THEY HAVE BEEN TAMPERED WITH.**

5. **At the end of lab, discuss your findings with your group or the class and write out any conclusions that can be drawn from your data.** Clearly state if you can reject any of your hypotheses, or if any of them are supported.

6. **Have your TA initial your notebook at the end of lab.** Your TA will check your notebooks later in the semester, and if entries are not initialed no credit will be given.

BSCI 105

The Scientific Method

The most critical concepts that any scientist has to master are those involved in the formulation and testing of hypotheses. To answer a scientific question in an effective manner, the question must be well thought out and carefully posed. Conversely, a poorly posed question may lead to a misinterpretation of the results or no results at all. Exercise 6 is designed to help you understand these concepts and the practical application of the scientific method. At this point **you should have also read over the material in the textbook that addresses the scientific method.** In Exercise 6, you will be asked to formulate hypotheses and to test those hypotheses. In each case, you will use what is known as the **scientific method** to pose and answer your questions.

BSCI 105

The Scientific Method and Scientific Communication

BSCI 105

Science increases our understanding of the world and the mechanisms that make it work. The **scientific method** is a formal process for answering questions about the world objectively, efficiently, and clearly. The process of the scientific method, also called hypothesis testing, is outlined below. It is critical that you understand this process because you will be applying it throughout the rest of the semester.

1. The first step in the scientific method is to **observe** a process, ask questions about it, and do background research on what is already known about the process.

2. Once a particular question has been identified, the next step is to formulate a clear, testable **hypothesis**. A hypothesis is a statement of what you believe is the cause of the observed phenomenon of interest. A key feature of a good hypothesis is that it generates reasonable **predictions** and is **testable**.

3. Design and conduct **experiments** based on the predictions generated by the hypothesis. Include appropriate **controls**. This approach to experimentation is called **hypothesis testing**.

4. Analyze the data from the experiments to determine if there is **support** for the hypothesis. If the hypothesis is **rejected**, the next step is to **modify** the hypothesis and repeat the process.

5. Once strong support for a hypothesis has been established, a final critical step is to **communicate** the experimental results and their interpretation with the broader scientific community.

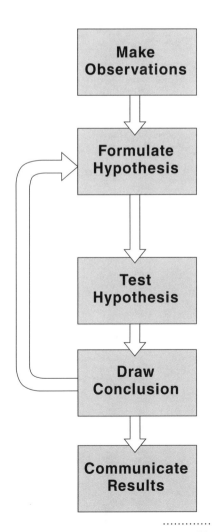

You will notice that the final component of the scientific method is the communication of your results and conclusions. It does not matter if that communication is through a report, paper, talk, or poster, but it is absolutely critical that results contribute to the ever-growing and constantly evolving body of scientific knowledge. Communication is the difference between science and hobby.

The Scientific Method and Scientific Communication

As described in the Lab Report Guide at the beginning of this lab manual, science writing is organized in a way that parallels the scientific method. The following procedure is intended to help you think about this relationship and how it impacts your lab report writing. A very important aspect of science is the concept of attribution, or the accurate referencing of sources of information. Not only does this give credit to the people who did the work, but it also allows readers to go back and look at those sources for themselves. Related to this is the issue of **plagiarism**, examples of which will be reviewed in the second procedure.

Below is an example of the practical application of the scientific method in a "real-life" situation. Read through it and see if you can clearly identify the basic steps described on the previous page.

Using the Scientific Method in Everyday Life

When driving to Ft. Lauderdale for spring break, you notice that your new SUV is getting much worse gas mileage than it did the week before. What could be causing the problem? You examine your car carefully. One difference that you notice immediately is the 12 friends that you now have crammed into the back of the car, most of whom were not present on your daily runs to and from campus. Perhaps the additional weight is the problem. You formulate the following hypothesis:

INCREASED LOAD IN THE CAR CAUSES INCREASED GAS CONSUMPTION IN YOUR SUV.

Is this hypothesis testable under the given conditions? You determine that it is. So, at the next fuel stop, you note the odometer reading and the amount of fuel you put into the gas tank. You then drive 200 miles. At the next stop you note the odometer reading, the amount of fuel you purchase, and calculate the gas mileage. Then, you sneak back to the car and ditch your friends while they are buying cheese curls.

After the next 200 miles, you stop, refuel, and compare the gas mileage of your car with and without your friends. Sure enough, your gas mileage has increased, but not substantially! There must be another factor involved. You think and observe and suddenly realize that the surfboard you have strapped to the roof may be a problem as well. A new, adjusted hypothesis can now be formulated:

INCREASED LOAD AND INCREASED WIND FRICTION CAUSE INCREASED GAS CONSUMPTION IN YOUR SUV.

To test this adjusted hypothesis, you slide your board into the back of the SUV (there's plenty of room now) and continue on your way, making the same odometer and fuel consumption observations that you made previously. When you arrive in Ft. Lauderdale, you note that your gas mileage has returned to normal, and your hypothesis is thus upheld! You conclude that both increased load and increased wind friction cause increased gas consumption in your SUV. Unfortunately, you found out too late that wind friction was a bigger factor than load in the reduction of fuel efficiency. Without your friends to chip in on gas money, you're tapped out and will have to bus tables at Denny's to make money for the trip back. Sometimes science can be brutal.

Procedure I: Scientific Writing Exercise

One member of your group will need to log on to ELMS/Blackboard to access the material for the next two exercises. After completing the online exercise your group should complete the Scientific Writing Worksheet and hand in one copy.

1. Log on to Blackboard and go to your lab section course space. Select the Lab Materials menu item, and open the Exercise 6A folder.

2. Launch the Scientific Writing Exercise Web page and read the instructions.

3. For each sentence you will need to decide, as a group, what part of a lab report it most likely belongs to. Once you have organized the sentences to your satisfaction you should complete Part A of the worksheet.

4. To complete Part B of the worksheet your group will need to agree what part of the scientific method each sentence best corresponds to.

Procedure II: Plagiarism Exercise

The Plagiarism Exercise is also launched from Blackboard, but it is a review exercise only with no assignment associated with it. You should read through it and discuss each question as a group. It is critical that you understand what constitutes plagiarism so you can recognize and avoid those costly errors in your lab reports. You can review this resource at any time.

Formulating and Testing Hypotheses

BSCI 105

Scenario

You are part of a research and development team for a major bread-producing company and have developed a new additive, 3B105, that creates a firmer, denser bread loaf, and greatly increases shelf life. The effects of the additive will allow this product to be shipped worldwide, thus expanding your company's international market share. Initial taste tests present a problem, however. Under controlled conditions, consumers reported a decrease in overall product satisfaction in the new bread versus bread made without the additive. Further market testing determines that the cause of this decrease in satisfaction is not the flavor, but rather the density and texture of the bread.

Knowing that your bread recipe consists primarily of flour, sugar, yeast, water, and salt, think about the following questions:

Which elements of the bread recipe are likely to influence the texture of the bread?

Which of these elements are likely to be significantly altered by the presence of an additive?

Which elements can you safely eliminate from your investigation?

Observations

The first step in the scientific method is to make objective observations about a phenomena or process of interest. Record all observations made in the Scenario in the box below:

Which **single ingredient** of bread do you think the additive 3B105 is **most likely** influenced?

Background—Cellular Respiration

Your team realizes that while many elements of the bread recipe might affect texture, the most sensitive part of the process is the leavening of the bread. That is, the process by which the bread dough "rises" prior to baking. Dough that does not rise properly would be small and dense, and would almost certainly have a noticeably different texture. Live yeast cultures present in the bread dough are responsible for providing leavening through the production of CO_2 gas, which causes the expansion of the dough. How do these yeast cells produce CO_2? Through the process of cellular respiration.

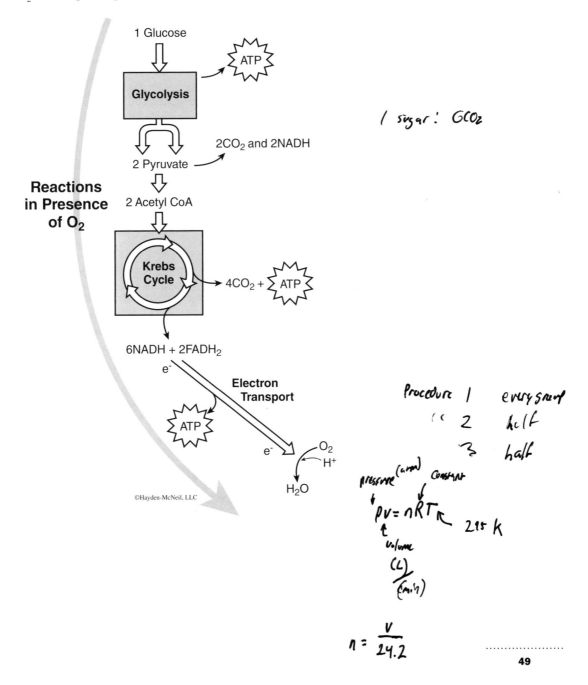

©Hayden-McNeil, LLC

1 sugar : $6CO_2$

Procedure 1 every smal
    " 2 half
      3 half

pressure (atm) constant

$pv = nRT$ 275 k

volume
(L)
(min)

$n = \dfrac{v}{24.2}$

In the presence of oxygen, yeast cells actively take up glucose and convert it to pyruvate, in a process known as **glycolysis**. The two pyruvate molecules that are produced from every one glucose molecule are then converted to acetyl CoA, which enters the **Krebs cycle**. A series of redox reactions transfer electrons to NAD^+ in order to produce NADH and $FADH_2$, which then transfers electrons to the **electron transport chain (ETC)**. Redox reactions that occur in the ETC yield H^+ that, ultimately, drive ATP synthase and the production of ATP. CO_2 and water are by-products of this reaction.

HYPOTHESES

Given what you know about cellular respiration, cells in general, and your own common sense, suggest three general **hypotheses** for the effect of the additive on the ingredient you chose.

Compare your suggestions to those of the other lab groups, discuss them, and as a class develop a consensus about **testable hypotheses** you should address.

METHODS

Your team must somehow assess the level of cellular respiration occurring in your baker's yeast cultures and compare it to that of cultures grown in the presence of 3B105. Two major ways to measure respiratory rate are proposed: 1) measure the disappearance of glucose from the starting solution, which would determine if glucose is being taken up, or 2) measure the production of CO_2 which would demonstrate that the output of the respiratory pathway is normal.

The reagents to measure glucose uptake are expensive, time-consuming, and require special handling, while measurements of CO_2 production can be performed relatively quickly and inexpensively. Which method do you recommend to your team and why?

What **variables** will you measure in your experiments to test your hypotheses?

In Part I of this exercise you will conduct an experiment to determine the rate of CO_2 production in yeast cultures with or without the 3B105 additive (the treatment). Ultimately you are interested in making statements about glucose metabolism, so you will need to convert measured rates of CO_2 production to rates of glucose metabolism. In Part II, you will learn about statistical methods for describing and comparing data that will help you draw informed conclusions about your hypotheses. Remember, your goal is to be able to make informed recommendations to your supervisor at the bread company, based on sound scientific evidence.

Background Part I

How can we determine the rate of glucose metabolism from data on CO_2 production? Hopefully, you will remember two important items:

First, the process of cellular respiration completely converts the carbon from 1 molecule of glucose to 6 molecules of CO_2.

Second, there is an equation called the Ideal Gas Law for converting the volume of a gas (such as CO_2) to the number of molecules of gas present:

$$PV = nRT \quad OR \quad n = PV \, / \, RT$$

Where:

P = pressure (in atmospheres)
T = temperature (in degrees Kelvin)
R = gas constant (0.08206 L atm/mol K)
V = volume (in liters)
n = number of molecules (moles)

Now, the Ideal Gas Law works just as well when volume (V) is expressed as a rate (liters per minute), which means we can easily convert rate of CO_2 gas production in ml/min to moles/min. To get rate of glucose metabolism, also in moles per minute, we simply divide by six!

Note that for most applications you can assume **P** = 1 atm and room temperature, **T** = 295 °K.

Procedure I: Measuring Yeast Metabolism via CO_2 Production

The class will be divided into five groups, each of which will set up two yeast **respirometers** containing yeast, either treated with 3B105 (experimental) or untreated (control). The different members within each group should set up and run the condition that they have been assigned (treated or control). The procedure is the same for each condition.

1. **Pipet 5 ml of glucose solution into a 50 ml beaker.** Select either "control" or "experimental" solution as appropriate. The experimental solution has 3B105 added.

2. *At the same time as your groupmates* (who are setting up the other condition) **use a 10 ml pipette to transfer 5 ml of the yeast suspension** into the flask. It is important for treated and untreated yeast to be added to their glucose solutions at the same time!

3. **Incubate for 5 minutes** at room temperature, with occasional swirling.

4. **Take up exactly 3 ml of the yeast/glucose mixture** into one of the syringes provided. Invert the syringe and draw 1 ml of air above the liquid. *Keep the remaining yeast suspensions for Procedures II and III!*

5. **Complete the assembly** of the respiration apparatus as shown in the figure. Add a small droplet to a 2 ml pipette and connect the pipette to the top of the syringe (no needle is present). Place the whole apparatus, upright, into a beaker.

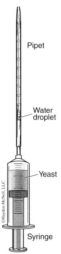

Pipet

Water droplet

Yeast

©Hayden-McNeil, LLC

Syringe

6. **As soon as the water droplet reaches the 0 ml mark, begin taking measurements at 2-minute intervals** and record the data in the table provided. You can mark measurements using either the top or the bottom of the droplet, but be sure to be consistent throughout the experiment. **Collect at least eight measurements** (see Sample Raw Data on the following page).

Time (min)	Reading (mls)	
	Treated	Untreated
0	0	0
2	0	0.02
4	0.015	0.05
6	0.02	0.09
8	0.04	0.16
10	0.065	0.24
12	0.10	0.32
14	0.14	0.40
16	0.18	0.51
18	0.23	0.61
20	0.26	0.70

7. **Plot the raw data** on the graph provided and draw a line through the linear portion of the curve (see Sample Raw Data Graph, below).

8. **Using only the linear part of the data, calculate the slope of the line** as change in volume ÷ change in time. This yields the rate of respiration in units of mls CO_2/minute.

9. **Convert the rate of CO_2 production (ml/min) to rate of glucose metabolism (moles/min).** Record these values in Table I.

10. **Enter the rates of glucose metabolism for control and treated yeast from your group in the spreadsheet provided, and record the class means and standard errors in Table I.** You will learn more about how to interpret these values in Part II.

$$\frac{0.45 - 0}{14 - 0} = 0.032 \frac{mL}{min}$$

$$\frac{0.032 \, mL}{min} \cdot \frac{1 \, L}{1000 \, mL} \cdot \frac{1}{24.2}$$

$$1.332 \times 10^{-6} \, mol \, CO_2 \cdot \frac{1}{6}$$

Table I. Rate of glucose metabolism in control and treated yeast.

Rate (moles/min) Control	Rate (moles/min) Treated	Class Mean Control	Standard Error Control	Class Mean Treated	Standard Error Treated
2.22×10^{-7}	1.17×10^{-7}				

Sample Raw Data

Time (min)	Reading (ml)
0	0.0
2	0.19
4	0.21
6	0.36
8	0.55
10	0.69
12	0.92

Sample Plot of Data

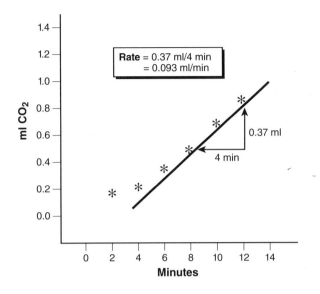

Construct a graph of your data here:

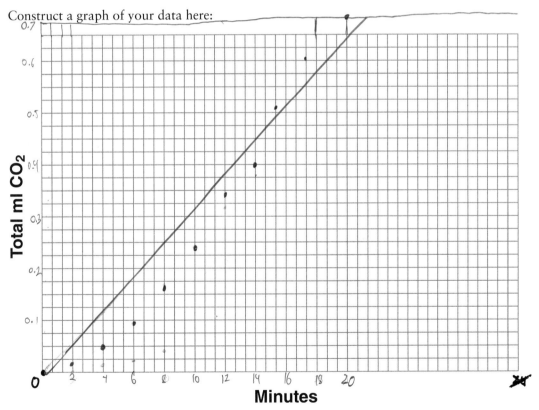

Hopefully, one of your hypotheses has something to do with 3B105 interfering with glucose metabolism by yeast. Two alternative hypotheses you should also have thought of have nothing to do with metabolism per se, but rather the cells themselves. It should be obvious after a moment's consideration that CO_2 would be reduced if 3B105 were either inhibiting cell division or outright killing cells. In either case, fewer cells equals less gas production without a direct effect on cellular metabolism.

Procedure II: Determining Relative Cell Number

Yeast (and other single cell organisms with a cell wall) will absorb light in proportion to the number or **density** of cells when suspended in media. The spectrophotometer can be used to measure the optical density of a yeast suspension as a measure of cell density.

1. **Make a "blank" with 3 ml yeast buffer in a clean cuvette.** Seal the top of the cuvette with Parafilm and mix well by inverting several times.

2. **Dilute 300 μl control yeast in 3 ml yeast buffer in a cuvette.** Blank the spectrophotometer and determine the absorbance at 630 nm. Record the absorbance of the control in Table II.

3. **Dilute the treated yeast suspension exactly the same as the control and measure its absorbance at 630 nm.** Record this value in Table II.

Table II. Yeast cell suspensions, absorbance at 630 nm.

A_{630} Control	A_{630} Treated	Class Mean Control	Standard Error Control	Class Mean Treated	Standard Error Treated
0.864	0.383				

4. **Enter your data in the spreadsheet provided and record the means and standard errors for the class in Table II.**

Procedure III: Determining Relative Cell Viability

Living cells have mechanisms to actively and passively exclude solutes in the extracellular environment from entering the cell. When a cell dies, these mechanisms fail and solutes rapidly accumulate in the cytoplasm. We can take advantage of this property to design "live-dead" cell assays based on the uptake of dyes by dead cells.

1. **For each of the control and treated yeast suspensions mix 40 µl with 960 µl of methylene blue solution in two microcentrifuge tubes.** Mix the cell suspension thoroughly with the dye.

2. **Mark your tubes with your group number and place them in the centrifuge.** The TA will centrifuge the samples for 5 minutes.

3. **Collect your tubes, being careful not to disturb the cell pellet.** You should have a light blue solution with a dark blue cell pellet.

4. **Gently pipette the solutions into clean cuvettes and mix each one with 1 ml water.**

5. **Measure the absorbance of each solution at 550 nm, and record your data in Table III.**

Table III. Yeast absorbed methylene blue solutions, absorbance at 550 nm.

A_{550} Control	A_{550} Treated	Class Mean Control	Standard Error Control	Class Mean Treated	Standard Error Treated
0.482	0.920				

6. **Enter your data in the spreadsheet provided and record the means and standard errors for the class in Table III.**

Background Part II
STATISTICAL ANALYSIS OF SAMPLED DATA

Once you have collected your data and determined your rates of glucose metabolism, relative cell density, and relative cell death, you will pool the class data and compare the data from the treated yeast with those from the control yeast. When examining numerical data taken from two or more samples, an investigator must consider the variability of the system and the measurements.

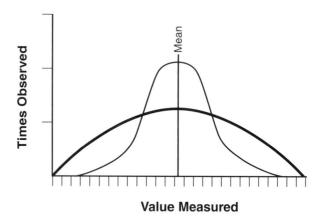

In most cases, a plot of data (e.g., glucose metabolism rates vs. frequency of observations) yields a bell-shaped curve with a maximum frequency at the average (mean) value. This curve is called a **normal distribution**. Note that the values obtained do not always yield the true value of the population mean. They may fall anywhere on the normal distribution curve. However, as sample size increases our estimate of the true mean will become less variable and more accurate.

Two sets of data with the same mean could have very different distributions (spread) on either side of the mean (see thin line versus thick line on the above graph). Conversely, two sets of data with somewhat different means may have so much spread as to be indistinguishable from one another arithmetically (see below).

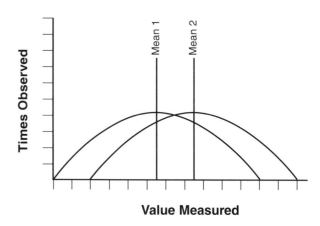

What are some reasons for variability in a set of data? How might it relate to variability in the biological system being examined?

How do we begin to determine whether the difference between two sets of data is real? To start, we will calculate the **standard deviation** of each data set, which is a numerical representation of the spread within the data. Using the standard deviation, we can then calculate the **standard error of the mean,** another measure of variability in a data set. It is this value that you may remember hearing described in voting tallies and other polls as "plus or minus" a certain number. The standard error of the mean is an estimate of how accurately our sample mean approximates the true mean of our population.

Examine the data presented here (number of flowers on treated versus untreated plants). The standard errors of the mean (or simply, "standard errors") were calculated for the two data sets and the data plotted on a bar graph. Then, the numerical value of the standard error was used to create the error bars that extend above and below the top of the data bar. In this case, the standard error for the treated plants is +/– 4.0 and the standard error for the untreated plants is +/– 1.8. Notice that the error bars do not overlap in space (see dotted lines). There are many formal statistical tests to determine if two samples are **significantly different**, but for purposes of this exercise, we will rely on "occular statistics." In general, if the standard errors of two samples do not overlap, they are likely to be significantly different.

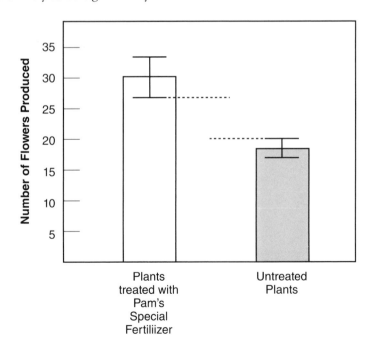

The error bars for the treated plants are bigger than for the untreated plants. What does this tell us about those data?

Procedure: Comparisons of Sample Means

1. One person from your group should enter your rates of glucose metabolism (Table I), relative cell densities (A_{630}, Table II), and relative cell viabilities (A_{525}, Table III) in the spreadsheet provided. Include both control and treated samples.

2. Record the class means and standard errors for each measure in Tables I–III.

3. For the rate of glucose metabolism, plot a bar graph using the means with error bars equal to plus and minus one standard error (± 1 SE). Using what you've learned from graphing these data, see if you can judge the other two measures just from looking at the tables (II and III).

4. Decide if the treated yeast are statistically different from the control for each measure. Discuss with the rest of the class the star points below.

Is more than one measure significantly different?

Do you think the magnitude of any differences in cell number or viability are sufficient to account for any observed difference in glucose metabolism?

Can more than one hypothesis be supported at the same time?

What is your conclusion about the effects of 3B105 on CO_2 production by yeast? Are there other possibilities than the ones examined in this exercise?

How might you recommend the company compensate for the effect of 3B105 during the bread making process?

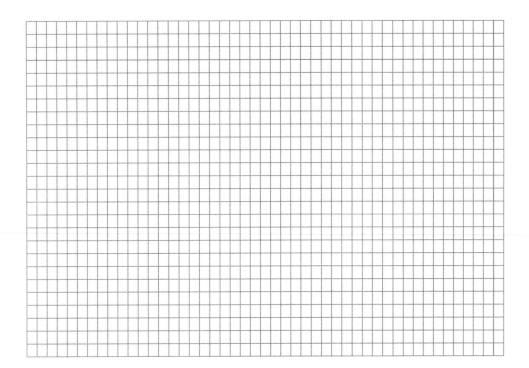

BSCI 105

Protocol Development, Optimization, and Application

The next three exercises address a very important subject in biology: enzyme kinetics. The concepts presented here are applicable to biologists in a variety of fields spanning ecology, medicine, and cell and molecular biology. Other important concepts covered here include the establishment and use of a standard curve and the influence of pH on biological systems. As you learn the basic concepts behind the function and regulation of enzyme activity in a biological system, you will also be asked to refine your laboratory and investigative skills. In Exercise 7, you will work to establish a protocol for assessing the activity of a well-known enzyme, alkaline phosphatase. In Exercise 8, you will optimize that protocol and apply it to test enzyme activity under various pH conditions. In Exercise 9, you will develop an assay to detect differences in enzyme variants using protein electrophoresis.

BSCI 105

Development of a Spectrophotometric Assay

for Alkaline Phosphatase

Scenario

Metabolic acidosis is a physiological condition that arises from a failure to regulate the acid–base balance in the blood. There are a variety of conditions that can cause metabolic acidosis, including dietary acid loading, diabetes, kidney failure, and respiratory distress, among others. Long-term metabolic acidosis can cause an imbalance in mineral homeostasis leading to depletion of hypoxyapetite and loss of bone density.

As a student laboratory assistant working under Dr. Imma Phicsion, you have been measuring serum alkaline phosphatase levels in diabetic teenagers with moderate kidney dysfunction leading to metabolic acidosis. Dr. Phicsion believes that inhibition of the **alkaline phosphatase** enzyme in osteoblasts by high acidity may be a primary cause of reduced bone density in this population.

While analyzing the measurements from 1,500 samples, you notice that 17 of the patients don't exhibit any change in alkaline phosphatase despite having significantly increased blood acidity. You bring these cases to the attention of Dr. Phicsion. After much head scratching and inspection of the data, Dr. Phicsion decides to examine these unusual cases more closely. She quickly discovers that those individuals are heterozygous for a mutation in the alkaline phosphatase protein that might cause the enzyme to misfold.

Dr. Phicsion credits your keen observational and analytical skills for the discovery of this mutant enzyme and decides to give you the opportunity to investigate its function under acidic conditions. You are assigned the task of putting together a team to develop a standardized assay for alkaline phosphatase function and to determine if the misfolded enzyme behaves differently from the normal enzyme.

Where do you begin? Familiarize yourself with the material on **chemical energy, catalysis,** and **enzymes.** To be certain that you understand the concepts presented, be able to answer the following questions:

1. To what class of organic molecules do enzymes belong?

2. What is the tertiary level of protein organization?

3. What conditions affect protein folding?

4. What conditions affect enzyme function?

5. In terms of amino acid sequence, how would an abnormal enzyme differ from a normal enzyme?

6. If you wanted to test an enzyme's activity, what would you measure?

Background

The above questions have reminded your laboratory team that enzymes are proteins, and as such, work best at particular ionic concentrations, at certain temperatures and in specific pH ranges. To determine whether the patients' alkaline phosphatase (AP) functions in an abnormal way, you could begin by testing their enzyme's activity at various pH levels. After looking through the medical literature, you discover that the human AP enzyme has its optimal activity at a pH of 10. If the AP present in the patients' blood functions at an optimum pH other than 10, then that version of the enzyme is functionally abnormal. Before you can begin such an analysis, however, a number of logistical questions must be answered.

Question #1: How can we test the activity of alkaline phosphatase?

Research has demonstrated that AP can remove a phosphate group from a molecule. On hand in the laboratory is a chemical named p-nitrophenyl phosphate (or PNP). When PNP is incubated with AP, the AP removes the phosphate group (PO_4) and the resulting molecule is called p-nitrophenol. Thus, PNP acts as an artificial substrate (i.e., a substrate not present in the human body) for AP.

The equation below shows the reaction.

O₂N—⬡—PO₄ **AP**→ O₂N—⬡—OH + PO₄

p-nitrophenyl phosphate (PNP)   *p*-nitrophenol + Pi
(colorless)   (yellow)

AP cleaves the phosphate group from the colorless pPNP ring yielding a yellow-colored *p*-nitrophenol molecule and a free phosphate group.

Two methods can be employed to determine activity. You can either measure how fast the substrate (PNP) is disappearing or measure how fast the product (*p*-nitrophenol) is forming. Looking at the equation, the team notices that the substrate is colorless while the product is yellow. The team decides to measure the formation of the product. Why?

 What piece of laboratory equipment can be used to determine the concentration of a colored solution?

The most obvious answer to the previous Star Points question is: the spectrophotometer. We can use the spectrophotometer to obtain OD readings of the yellow colored product and then convert those readings into concentration, using **Beer's law**. Two important questions must be answered before we can do this.

Question #2: What is the optimal wavelength for measuring the reaction product? (Setting up an absorption spectrum)

Question #3: How do we convert OD readings to specific concentrations? (Establishing a standard curve)

The Absorbance Spectrum

In order to set the spectrophotometer at the optimal wavelength for measuring the concentration of our reaction product, we must establish an **absorbance spectrum**. That is, we will measure a sample of the reaction product (*p*-nitrophenol) at various wavelengths and determine which wavelength provides the optimal absorption. That wavelength is then used to find the OD values of the experimental reaction products.

To construct an absorption spectrum, absorption readings are taken every 25 nanometers and the resulting OD values are plotted. When a peak is found, readings are taken in 5 nanometer increments around the peak. This procedure pinpoints the wavelength best absorbed by the *p*-nitrophenol solution.

*If the product is yellow, what color light is **not** absorbed by p-nitrophenol? (Hint: See Exercise 2.)*

The Standard Curve

After the peak absorbance has been determined, the spectrophotometer is set to that wavelength. A series of known concentrations of *p*-nitrophenol is made and their OD values are read on the spectrophotometer. A graph of the known concentrations against their OD readings is plotted. This graph is a standard curve and should yield a straight line. From this standard curve we can determine the **extinction coefficient**.

 The extinction coefficient can be determined from the standard curve. How is this accomplished?

Procedure: Absorbance Spectrum

To determine the appropriate wavelength of light to use in our AP experiment, perform the following simple procedure:

1. **Obtain two clean spectrophotometer cuvettes and label them with tape near the top of each tube.** Handle cuvettes with care, and avoid getting fingerprints on the bottom half—it is a good idea to clean them with Kimwipes before you use them.

    To one cuvette, add 0.25 ml of the colorless substrate, PNP, 0.25 ml pH 10 buffer, and 5.0 ml 0.05 N NaOH. This will serve as the blank, which contains everything except the product, *p*-nitrophenol.

    To the second cuvette, add 0.25 ml PNP, 0.25 ml pH 10 buffer, and 5.0 ml of the yellow product solution, *p*-nitrophenol. You will use this tube to generate the absorbance spectrum of *p*-nitrophenol.

     Why is the PNP solution the blank?

2. Place the PNP cuvette into the spectrophotometer and set the instrument to 0.000 absorbance at a wavelength of 400 nm (save the blank for the next procedure).

3. Insert the cuvette containing *p*-nitrophenol and read the absorbance.

4. Now increase the wavelength at 25 nm increments, zero the spectrophotometer at each new wavelength using the blank, and record the resulting absorbances for *p*-nitrophenol in Table I. Stop at 700 nm.

Table I. *p*-Nitrophenol Absorption Spectrum

Wavelength (nm)	Absorbance (OD)	
	PNP (Blank)	*p*-nitrophenol
400 nm	0.0	0.206
425 nm	0.0	0.133
450 nm	0.0	0.020
475 nm	0.0	0.004
500 nm	0.0	0.002
525 nm	0.0	0.007
550 nm	0.0	0.000
575 nm	0.0	-0.012
600 nm	0.0	-0.008
625 nm	0.0	-0.008
650 nm	0.0	0.005
675 nm	0.0	-0.001
700 nm	0.0	0.014
Additional Wavelengths Around Peak (5 nm Intervals)		
405 nm	0.0	0.185
410 nm	0.0	0.171
415 nm	0.0	0.143
420 nm	0.0	0.142

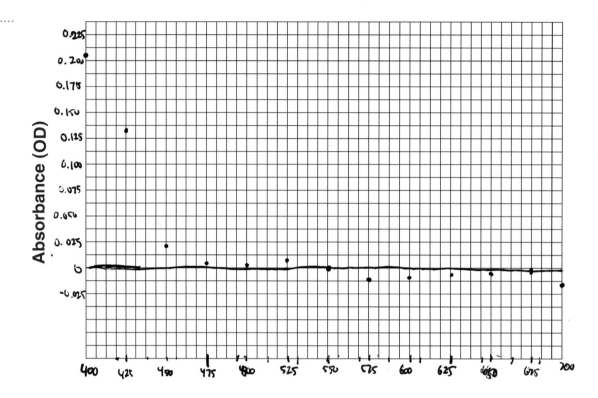

Wavelength (nm)

5. Transfer your OD values for PNP and *p*-nitrophenol to graph paper. (NOTE: The graph paper in this manual is provided for obtaining a quick sketch of your results. **It is not to be used in a final report.**) From your sketch, determine the range of optimum wavelengths.

6. Obtain the absorption spectrum at 5 nm intervals within this range in order to more precisely identify the optimum wavelength.

 What wavelength of light should be used to measure the amount of p-nitrophenol formed during the reaction? What is the reason for this choice?

Procedure: Standard Curve

To construct your standard curve for *p*-nitrophenol, you will make a series of dilutions of *p*-nitrophenol. You will dilute the *p*-nitrophenol in NaOH, buffer and PNP solution.

1. **Retrieve the blank that you made for the previous procedure.** Use this to set the absorbance of the spectrophotometer to 0.000 at the optimal wavelength (as determined above).

2. **Label a series of cuvettes from #2 to #6 and** *accurately* **pipette the proper amounts of the following solutions into these tubes:**

Tube #	*p*-nitrophenol (ml)	0.05N NaOH (ml)	pH 10 Buffer (ml)	PNP (ml)	Final [*p*-nitrophenol]
2	0.5	4.5	0.25	0.25	0.01 µmole/ml
3	1.0	4.0	0.25	0.25	0.02 µmole/ml
4	2.0	3.0	0.25	0.25	0.04 µmole/ml
5	3.0	2.0	0.25	0.25	0.06 µmole/ml
6	4.0	1.0	0.25	0.25	0.08 µmole/ml

3. **Remove the blank cuvette from the spectrophotometer.**

4. **Put cuvette #2 into the spectrophotometer, and determine the absorbance of this standard solution containing 0.01 µmole/ml of** *p*-nitrophenol. Record the absorbance in Table II, on the next page.

5. **Measure the absorbance of the next higher concentration of *p*-nitrophenol.** Repeat this procedure until the absorbances of all of the standard solutions have been recorded.

6. **Use these data to construct your standard curve.** Plot the *p*-nitrophenol concentrations in μmole/ml on the x-axis and the corresponding absorbances on the y-axis. Draw a line of best fit through your data points, starting at (0,0).

 Why does a standard curve always intersect the axes at point (0,0)?

Table II. *p*-Nitrophenol Standard Curve

Concentration (μmole/ml)	Absorbance (OD)
0.00	0
0.01	0.043
0.02	0.078 1
0.04	0.118
0.06	0.126
0.08	0.187
Value of **e** (from plot of data on next page) = 2.226	

The slope of the resulting line is the extinction coefficient (e in the Beer's law equation). After determining the slope, you may use Beer's law to calculate an unknown concentration of *p*-nitrophenol from a known absorbance. This is a very useful property. In next week's assay of the patients' AP activity, you will determine the absorbances of the product formed (i.e., *p*-nitrophenol) and use this standard curve and Beer's law to calculate the corresponding concentrations.

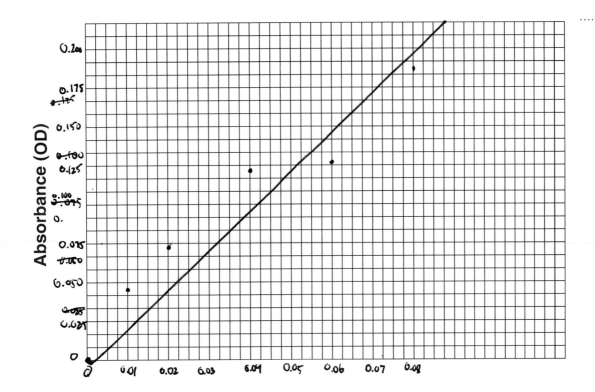

Absorbance (OD)

[*p*-nitrophenol] (µmoles/ml)

BSCI 105

Determining the pH Optimum of Alkaline Phosphatase

BSCI 105

Scenario

After reporting the progress of your team in establishing a spectrophotometric assay for the AP enzyme, you are given the green light to proceed with your experiment using valuable patient protein samples. However, before she will give you the samples, Dr. Phicsion insists that you state the hypothesis to be tested clearly, incorporating the information gained from your previous tests.

Write a precise hypothesis in the box below.

```
+-----------------------------------------------+
|                                               |
|                                               |
|                                               |
|                                               |
|                                               |
|                                               |
+-----------------------------------------------+
```

Background

To perform this week's exercise, you will need certain data that you obtained in last week's exercise.

The maximum wavelength absorbed by *p*-nitrophenol. (This will be the wavelength you set the spectrophotometer to this week.) _____ nm

The value of the extinction coefficient for *p*-nitrophenol. (You will use this to determine concentration of product formed in the pH optimum experiment.)

$$e = \underline{\hspace{2cm}}$$

Having obtained this information, we are nearly ready to run the experimental samples, but we still need to answer one more important question.

Question #4: Over what length of time should the reaction occur? (Establishing a time course)

In order for the pH experiment to yield useful data, the optimum length of incubation needs to be determined and then held constant for every pH. To figure out the optimum incubation period, a **time course** is constructed.

This week the laboratory staff will determine the incubation time for the pH experiment and will then carry out that experiment. You will initiate the AP assay by mixing the enzyme solution with an abundance of the *p*-nitrophenyl phosphate (PNP) substrate. As the enzyme removes the phosphate from PNP, the resulting yellow product, *p*-nitrophenol, is formed.

Plot the expected formation of p-nitrophenol (yellow color) over time. (Hint: If you are having trouble thinking about it, ask yourself, "What happens to the total amount of product formed as the substrate is used up"?)

What would the graph look like if the amount of enzyme was doubled in the above experiment?

What would happen to the graph if the amount of substrate was decreased at the beginning of the experiment?

Formation of *p*-nitrophenol (μm/ml)

Time (minutes)

The slope of this graph is expressed in units of **velocity** (or rate of the reaction). If an excess of substrate is present at the start of the incubation of the enzyme with the substrate, most enzymes will form product at a constant rate over time. This constant rate yields the straight line portion of the graph and it is called the **initial velocity** or V_0. As the enzyme uses up the substrate, the rate of product formation decreases and the straight line begins to curve and then to level off. If you want to measure AP activity, at which portion of the curve (or at which point in time) will you read the absorbance of the product?

If you wait too long, the excess substrate has been used up and the amount of product formed is no longer proportional to the enzyme activity. If you don't wait long enough, you may not have enough product formed to measure accurately. You also don't want to wait all day. The scientists must blend the needs of the experiment with the practical needs. Therefore, your first experiment will be to determine the **time course** of AP activity which entails measuring AP activity over time.

OVERVIEW OF THE EXPERIMENTAL PROCEDURE

The basic steps of this procedure are as follows: First, you will take a series of test tubes and add pH 10 buffer and the substrate PNP. Then you will incubate the tubes for increments of five minutes. All tubes will be placed in the incubator (in this case a warm water bath of 37 °C) and allowed to sit for five minutes. This allows all the tubes to warm to the temperature optimum of AP.

AP is then added (at the same time) to each tube, and every five minutes one tube will be removed and tested. Thus the first tube will be removed after a total of ten minutes in the bath (5 minutes to warm up and 5 minutes for the AP to work). The next tube is removed after a total of 15 minutes in the bath (5 minutes to warm up and 10 minutes for the AP to work). The other tubes are removed after 20 and 25 total minutes in the bath. The specific details of this procedure are given below:

Procedure: Determining the Optimal Timecourse

1. **Make the blank: Add 0.25 ml (250 µl) of substrate (PNP) solution, 0.25 ml of pH 10 buffer, and 5.0 ml of 0.05 N NaOH to a clean cuvette.** (Note: AP itself cannot be added to the blank because it may cause a brief color reaction to occur. The small amount of water added with the AP will not significantly alter the blank, therefore the AP solution is not included in the blank.) Use this **blank** to set the spectrophotometer to 0.000 absorbance.

2. **To a series of five clean cuvettes, add 0.25 ml of substrate PNP and 0.25 ml of pH 10 buffer.** Place them into a warm water (37 °C) bath. Record the time this step is completed _____. After waiting for 5 minutes, **quickly** add 0.1 ml (100 μl) of enzyme (AP) solution to each tube and rapidly mix the solutions by gently shaking the tubes. Immediately return the tubes to the water bath. A little team work will make the job much easier.

3. **After 5 minutes from the time you added the AP remove the first tube and add 5.0 ml of 0.05 N NaOH.** Mix the contents of the tube by covering the top with Parafilm and inverting. The NaOH stops the reaction.

Why is temperature an important aspect of the experiment?

Why does NaOH stop the reaction? (Hint: NaOH is very basic.)

4. **After 10 total minutes have passed take the second tube out and add 5.0 ml of 0.05 N NaOH and mix.** Do the same for the next tube at 15 minutes, and then 20 minutes, and for the last tube at 25 minutes.

5. **Measure the sample absorbances at the wavelength you chose from your absorption spectrum last week.** Remember to use the **blank** to set the initial absorbance to 0.000. (Save this blank; you will need it for the next part of the experiment below.) Record the sample absorbances (as OD units) in **Table I** and plot the results on the graph on the next page. Identify the linear portion of the graph.

Table I. AP Time Course

Time *Since* Addition of AP in Minutes (Time for AP to Work)	Absorbance (OD)
0	0
5	0.103 .123
10	0.195
15	0.279
20	0.393
25	0.368

Absorbance (OD)

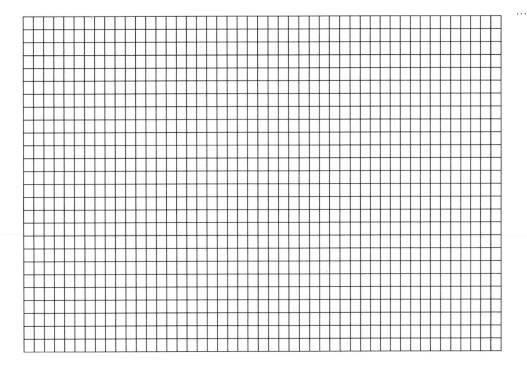

Time (minutes)

6. **Confer with your colleagues and select a suitable incubation time for the rest of your enzyme assays.** Remember your criteria are:

   - The time you choose should be in the linear portion of the curve.

   - At the time you choose enough product has been formed to give an OD reading of at least 0.1. (Less than that and you may have too much error for a good reading.)

   - The time you choose should be efficient for the researcher.

   Record the chosen incubation time here. _____

Procedure: Alkaline Phosphatase pH Optimum

Now that you have determined the optimal wavelength, extinction coefficient, and incubation time for your reaction, it is time to test your hypothesis. With this procedure you will determine the rate of conversion of PNP to *p*-nitrophenol by the alkaline phosphatase enzyme. You will collect and compare class data on the effect of pH on normal human AP and the mutant AP from the heterozygous patients.

The same procedure will be used to determine the **rate** of *p*-nitrophenol production using both normal and mutant AP. Record the data from your trials and the class means and standard errors in Tables II and III.

1. **Obtain six clean cuvettes. Add 0.25 ml of each of the pH buffers (pH 6.0, 7.0, 8.0, 9.0, 10, and 11) to separate test tubes.**

2. **Add 0.25 ml of substrate PNP to each cuvette.** Be sure to keep track of the tubes by labeling each one with tape. Use the blank from the previous experiment as the blank to adjust the spectrophotometer to 0.000 absorbance immediately before reading a sample.

3. **Place all six of the cuvettes into the 37 °C water bath and wait 5 minutes to allow the solution to equilibrate to 37 °C. Add 0.1 ml of enzyme solution (AP) to each cuvette, mix well and record the time. Add the enzyme to cuvettes at 2-minute intervals.**

4. **After incubating for the exact amount of time you chose, add 5.0 ml of 0.05 N NaOH to the cuvettes to terminate the enzyme reaction.** Read the absorbance of the solution, and record the value in **Table II or Table III**. Repeat the procedure for each of the other five pH values.

Table Ia. Normal AP Reactions

Tube # (pH):	6	7	8	9	10	11
Start time						
Stop time						

Table Ib. Mutant AP Reactions

Tube # (pH):	6	7	8	9	10	11
Start time	7:15	7:20	7:22	7:34	7:26	7:24
Stop time	7:25	7:30	7:32	7:44	7:36	7:34

Table II. Normal AP Activity as a Function of pH.

pH	Absorbance (OD)	Concentration (µmole/ml)	Rate (µmole/ml/min)	Class Mean Rate (µmole/ml/min)
6.0				~~0.0003~~ 0.0015
7.0				0.00184
8.0				0.0029
9.0				0.0054
10				0.0079
11				0.0098

Extinction coefficient (e)= ___2.226___   Incubation time = ___10 min.___

Table III. Mutant AP Activity as a Function of pH.

pH	Absorbance (OD)	Concentration (µmole/ml)	Rate (µmole/ml/min)	Class Mean Rate (µmole/ml/min)
6.0	0.555	0.247	0.025	0.196
7.0	0.858	0.385	0.035	0.0177
8.0	0.075	0.034	0.034	0.0140
9.0	0.025	0.011	0.011	0.0110
10	-0.003	-0.001	-0.0001	0.0008
11	0.025	0.0012	0.0012	0.0010

Extinction coefficient (e)= ___2.226___   Incubation time = ___10 min.___

5. After recording the absorbances of your six samples in Table II or III, use your standard curve from last week to convert OD units to concentration of *p*-nitrophenol product formed. Use Beer's law. Now divide the amount formed by the incubation time in minutes, and you have the **rate** of *p*-nitrophenol produced in µmole/ml/min for each of your pH values.

6. Collect the rates for normal and mutant AP enzymes from all of the groups in class and record the mean rate for each treatment in Tables II and III. Plot the mean rates for both enzymes on the graph paper provided on the next page. These are the pH **activity curves** for the two enzymes.

Data Interpretation
Examine your data and consider the following questions:

- At what pH did the patients' AP work best? How does that compare with normal human AP? What conclusions can you come to?

- Restate the hypothesis:

- Do these data support or refute your hypothesis?

- What future investigations would you recommend to Dr. Phicsion?

Make sure that you have recorded all data in your lab notebook!

Mean Rate of Activity (μmole/ml/min)

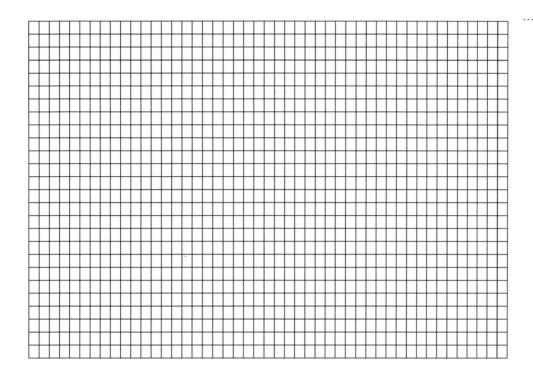

pH

BSCI 105

An Assay for Alkaline Phosphatase Variants Using SDS-PAGE

Scenario

Dr. Phicsion is thrilled by the success of your assay in demonstrating that there is a key functional difference between the normal and mutant variants of alkaline phosphatase from heterozygous individuals. Now she wants to see if you can develop an assay to detect these variants in the field using inexpensive and portable equipment. You suggest using polyacrylamide gel electrophoresis (PAGE) in combination with a test for catalytic activity similar to the *p*-nitrophenol assay.

Background

Many amino acids that are components of proteins carry either positive or negative charges (mainly as NH_3 or COO– groups). The overall charge of a protein depends on the relative frequency of charged amino acids, making them acidic (more negative) or basic (more positive). If proteins are exposed to an electrical current they will move towards the oppositely charge pole or electrode. This is the basis for techniques involving protein electrophoresis.

All else being equal, proteins will migrate at different rates depending on their overall charges, and acidic and basic proteins will move in opposite directions. When performing protein electrophoresis, a handy trick is to treat samples with the detergent **SDS**, which coats proteins and makes all charges negative. In the presence of SDS, all proteins will migrate in the same direction at a rate that is basically proportional to their size.

The most common medium for protein electrophoresis is **polyacrylamide**, which is a polymer of the two chemicals acrylamide and bis-acrylamide. Poly-acrylamide forms a gel with different sized pores that retard the movement of proteins, so small proteins move much faster than large proteins. This type of analysis is called polyacrylamide gel electrophoresis, or **PAGE**. When using SDS-coated proteins, it is called **SDS-PAGE**.

> **WE WILL BE USING PRE-CAST GELS, BUT UNPOLYMERIZED ACRYL-AMIDE IS A NEUROTOXIN, SO GLOVES SHOULD BE WORN AT ALL TIMES!**

Procedure

1. Your TA will set up the polyacrylamide gels and PAGE apparatus.

2. You TA will demonstrate how to load a PAGE gel using a pre-stained protein standard. The standard is composed of proteins of known size and can be used to estimate the sizes of sample proteins.

3. Each group will load three samples on the gels:
   a. Homozygous normal AP extract (10 µl)
   b. Heterozygous AP extract (10 µl)
   c. Purified mutant AP enzyme (10 µl)

4. After all of the samples are loaded, your TA will turn on the power supply and run the gel until the loading dye indicates it has gone far enough.

5. Your TA will open the gels, cut them, and transfer them to staining trays.

6. Get the tray with your samples and add 50 ml of **AP Buffer, pH 7**. Swirl the gel gently for two minutes to wash off the SDS.

7. Pour the buffer into the liquid waste beaker at your table.

8. Add 50 ml of AP Buffer, pH 7 to cover your gel.

9. Add 1 ml of **AP Substrate Solution** and swirl to mix.

10. Add 1 ml of **AP Dye Solution** and swirl to mix.

11. Put the lid on your staining tray and place it on the platform in the 37°C water bath to incubate. Swirl occasionally and remove the tray when distinct bands of color can be seen.

12. Pour off staining solution in waste beaker.

13. Add 50 ml **PBS** and swirl for two minutes to wash off excess staining solution.

14. Sketch your gel in your notebook, noting differences in position and intensity of bands.

15. Measure the distance traveled by each band in the protein standard, and note the molecular weight of each using the guide on the front bench.

16. Graph the distance traveled as a function of molecular weight of the protein standard bands on semi-log graph paper. Draw a standard curve.

17. Measure the distance traveled by the enzyme bands and plot them on your standard curve to estimate molecular weight.

 Did you observe a difference in size between the normal and mutant enzymes?

 Did you observe a difference in activity between the enzymes?

 Can you tell a homozygote from a heterozygote by looking at the gel?

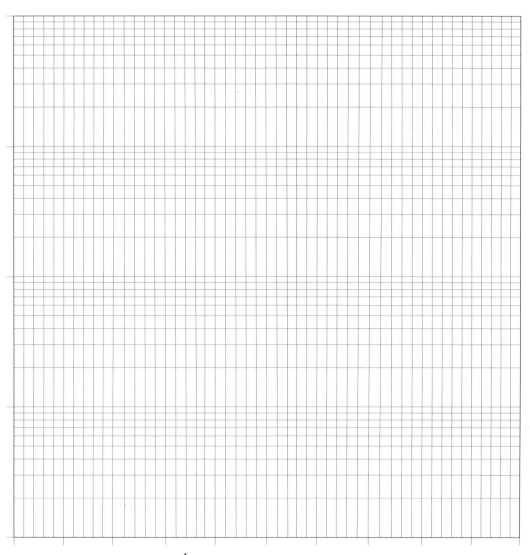

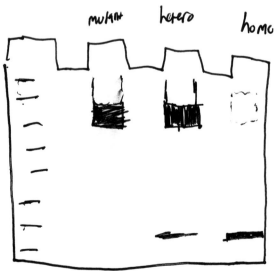

mutant   hetero   homo

Data Collection and Interpretation of Results

BSCI 105

Up to this point in the laboratory series, we have explored various aspects of experimental biology: the general structure of the scientific method, hypothesis testing, the correct way to construct a protocol, and the optimization of a scientific protocol. Now you are ready to focus on data collection and interpretation of your results. The following exercises are designed to be straightforward enough for you to run (possibly more than once) and collect relatively large amounts of data. In fact, the accuracy of the final analyses is dependent upon a large pool of data. Based on the results of these experiments, we expect you to come away with a solid knowledge of the manner in which experimental data are collected and recorded. In addition, you should be sure that you understand the various methods of analysis used in the molecular and cell biology laboratory.

- Lab report format
  - times, 12 pt., db. spaced
  - 4-6 pages w/ ~~page~~ figs. no min or max
  - 1" margins
  - page # lower right corner
  - title + abstract
  - Label: intro, methods, results, discussion, lit. cited

Characterization of DNA

DNA Analysis

BSCI 105

The next three exercises will introduce you to the common methods used for the analysis of DNA structure and function in the molecular biology laboratory. You will get hands on experience with the workhorse of molecular biology: the polymerase chain reaction (PCR). You will also learn how to isolate DNA from bacteria and how to analyze DNA using agarose gel electrophoresis. Finally you will see how sequences are identified using comparisons with public databases.

BSCI 105

DNA Analysis I

PCR, Plasmids, and Agarose Gel Electrophoresis

Scenario

As a pre-med student intern at Maryland Hope Hospital, you are assigned to "shadow" Dr. Michroba in the outpatient clinic. Dr. Michroba is concerned by a spike in cases of food poisoning caused by an unusual bacterium. Patient symptoms are consistent with *E. coli* contamination, as are tests on cultured bacteria that are positive for ability to metabolize both glucose and lactose. However, the PCR test to positively identify the strain of bacteria is consistent with *Salmonella* rather than *E. coli*, and the bacteria are resistant to ampicillin and related antibiotics. Dr. Michroba wants to know (1) if he is dealing with an atypical strain of *E. coli* that is giving a false positive on the PCR test, or a strain of lactose-metabolizing *Salmonella*; and (2) if the ampicillin resistance gene is integral to the bacterial genome or conferred by acquired plasmid DNA.

Dr. Michroba asks you to take samples of normal *E. coli* and of the unusual strain of bacteria, dubbed "MH1," to the lab for further characterization. He wants you to accomplish three important goals:

1. Confirm that the MH1 bacteria metabolize lactose and are ampicillin resistant.

2. Test PCR markers and use sequence analysis to positively identify MH1.

3. Determine if MH1 carries a plasmid that confers ampicillin resistance, and possibly to additional antibiotics.

E.oli   1 band
Sam.   3 bands

Background

A common source of food poisoning is ingestion of *E. coli* from contaminated raw foods. *E. coli* is a normal part of the intestinal microbial ecosystem but can be harmful to other parts of the digestive tract. These bacteria belong to a group called the *Enterobacteriaceae* that also includes less benign members such as *Salmonella*. A common clinical test to identify *E. coli* is the ability to metabolize the simple sugar lactose (lac+ but rare strains of *Salmonella* have evolved that are also lac+ and lead to misdiagnosis of cases of food poisoning. Molecular biology methods have proven useful in designing new, more specific tests for identifying clinically relevant bacterial strains.

The most powerful tool for this purpose has been **PCR**, the polymerase chain reaction, which allows selective amplification of the DNA for "markers" based on unique genes or sequence polymorphisms. PCR can multiply an individual gene into millions of copies very rapidly and provide enough DNA to easily analyze using agarose gel electrophoresis (Figure 1).

Additional tools such as the **DNA miniprep** allow the separate analysis of bacterial genomic DNA and plasmid DNA, which often is the source of rapidly evolving antibiotic resistance. Genomic DNA in bacteria typically consists of a single large, circular molecule that includes all of the required genes for the organism to function. Plasmids are small circular DNA molecules that are distinct from and supplemental to the gemonic DNA—they are not required but can provide additional material to improve the survival of the host bacteria.

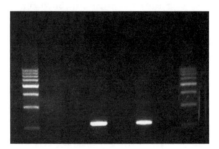

Figure 1. Example of plasmid DNA visualized using a fluorescent dye following gel electrophoresis. The first lane shows a DNA "ladder" of known size fragments that help determine the size of the plasmids being studied.

WHAT IS PCR?

The polymerase chain reaction, or PCR, uses the components of the native cellular DNA replication machinery to make copies of, or **amplify**, specific pieces of DNA. In a cell the DNA needs to be replicated, or copied, prior to each division. This is accomplished by the enzyme **DNA polymerase** that is recruited to short, complementary **primers** that bind to specific locations along the original DNA **template**. PCR uses a special polymerase enzyme (*Taq*) originally isolated from a heat-loving microbe. Unlike many enzymes, *Taq* can be heated repeatedly without denaturing, and is the basis for a technique call thermacycling. A mixture of template DNA, primers, nucleotides, and *Taq* is repeatedly heated and cooled so that new DNA copies are produced each cycle, amplifying the sequence of interest.

HOW DOES A PCR TEST WORK?

A "PCR test" is any assay that uses PCR to analyze a piece of DNA known to differ between genomes. A particular assay may test for presence/absence of a gene that is known to occur in one genome but not another, or it may be based on a **polymorphism** in a gene between different strains or associated with a disease. A polymorphism in the DNA sequence could make a primer no longer work so you either get amplification or you don't, or it may produce products that differ in length. Either result can be easily examined using gel electrophoresis.

This exercise will test for the presence/absence of three markers using a technique called **multiplex PCR**. The PCR master mix will contain three pairs of primers designed as follows:

- *gapA* Primers: Amplify a conserved enzyme common to all Enterobacteriaceae.

- *apE* Primers: Specific to a *Salmonella* endonuclease.

- *invA* Primers: Specific to a *Salmonella* virulence factor.

The *apE* primers gave the positive result in the PCR test for *Salmonella* using the MH1 bacterial strain. If that result is correct, the *invA* primers should also give a positive result.

WHAT IS A PLASMID MINIPREP?

Much of molecular biology is based a technique called **cloning** that involves isolating a gene or other piece of DNA, putting it into a plasmid, and using bacteria as little factories to make precise copies of the plasmid. If you want more plasmid, you simply grow more bacteria! To recover clean plasmid, getting rid of everything else, the miniprep is typically used. This technique involves four steps: (1) lysis of bacterial cells, (2) precipitation of DNA from the solution, (3) washing away lipids, proteins, RNA, and genomic DNA, and (4) resuspending the plasmid DNA in a small volume.

HOW DOES DNA ELECTROPHORESIS WORK?

Gel electrophoresis is used to separate DNA molecules by size, based on the fact that DNA has a negatively charged backbone and will move in an electric current. For DNA, a seaweed product called **agarose** is often used, as it forms a matrix suitable for separating a wide range of molecules. The agarose retards the movement of molecules in proportion to their size so small molecules move faster large molecules when an electric current is applied. A DNA-specific dye is added to the gel to make the different **bands** of DNA visible, and a **ladder** of known-size DNA fragments is used to judge the size of DNA molecules observed.

Procedure I. Lactose Metabolism and Ampicillin Resistance

Examine bacterial plates that have been inoculated with normal *E. coli* and the MH1 bacterial strain.

lac+

1. The plates have been treated with a dye that has a beta-galactosidic bond similar to that in lactose and can be digested by the *E. coli lacZ* gene product, the beta-galactosidase enzyme. In the presence of the dye, lac+ baterial colonies will become blue, while lac− colonies will remain white. What color are the colonies on the two plates? Are the MH1 colonies lac+ or lac−?

2. Antibiotic disks containing ampicillin have been added to the plates. Is there a difference in antibiotic resistance of the normal *E. coli* and the MH1 strain? How would you measure relative differences in antibiotic resistance?

Procedure II. Colony PCR

There are many methods to isolate and purify DNA from different cell types. Some "downstream" applications, such as restriction digests and gene cloning, require very clean DNA without contamination by lipids, polysaccharides, proteins, or RNA. Simple PCR for gel electrophoresis, on the other hand, is possible without purification as long as the target DNA is in solution and there is nothing present that will interfere with the DNA polymerase enzyme.

Colony PCR is a simple method that involves lysis of bacterial cells in water, which also dilutes cell debris and contaminants, followed directly by PCR and agarose gel electrophoresis.

1. Pipette 50 µL distilled water into a clean 1.5 ml microcentrifuge tube.

2. Open one of your bacterial growth plates and choose a colony.

3. Use a sterile toothpick to scrape/lift the colony off the agar plate.

4. Dip the tip of the toothpick with the colony in the water in your microcentrifuge tube and stir briskly for a few seconds. This is your **bacterial lysate**.

5. Close tube and discard toothpick properly.

6. Take your tube to the front of the room, and pipette ~~10~~ 8 µl of your bacterial lysate into one tube in a strip as directed by your TA.

7. Your TA will add 10 µl of 2X PCR Master Mix to each tube and seal the caps tightly. The strip of tubes will then be placed in the PCR machine (thermacycler) and run with the following program: *tube 8*

   Step 1. Enzyme activation: **95** °C for **5** minutes

   Step 2. Amplification: (~~33~~ **35** cycles)
   Denaturation   **96** °C for **5** seconds
   Annealing   **63** °C for **5** seconds
   Extension   72 °C   for **15** seconds

   Step 3. Final Extension: 72 °C   for three minutes

   → *Stop here*

8. When the program is complete, your TA will remove the tube strip from the PCR machine, cut off your tube, and give it to your group.

9. Add 4 µl of DNA Loading Dye to your tube and pipette up and down to thoroughly mix with your PCR product. *Check with your TA that this was not already included in the PCR master mix!*

10. Analyze reaction products by agarose gel electrophoresis.

Procedure III. Plasmid Miniprep

In this exercise you will isolate plasmid DNA from a culture of the MH1 bacterial strain. Culture media with ampicillin added was inoculated and grown overnight, resulting in a dense population of antibiotic resistant bacteria. You will use a plasmid DNA miniprep procedure to determine if the ampicillin resistant bacteria are carrying plasmid.

1. Place (1) two clean microcentrifuge tubes and (2) a miniprep column with collection tube in a rack.

2. Get one microcentrifuge tube and pipette 600 µl of bacterial culture provided.

3. Add 100 µl of 7X Lysis Buffer (blue) to your tube, and immediately cap the tube and turn upside down several times to mix. If all goes well, you should get a clear bluish solution.

4. Add 350 µl of *cold* Neutralization Buffer (yellow), and immediately cap tube and turn upside down several times to mix. A yellow precipitate should form and there should be no blue color left.

5. Use a disposable pipette to transfer the yellow solution (with precipitate) to a 2 ml filter syringe.

6. Hold the syringe over the miniprep column (in collection tube) and push in the plunger. You should get a clear yellow solution, with the precipitate stuck in the filter in the syringe.

7. Place the miniprep column with collection tube in the centrifuge and note the position number of your tube. The TA will operate the centrifuge once all groups are ready.

8. Following centrifugation, recover your miniprep column and collection tube.

9. Transfer your miniprep column to a clean microcentrifuge tube.

10. Carefully pipette 30 µl of Elution Buffer onto the white filter in the miniprep column. Do not poke the filter!

11. Let the column stand for 1 minute. This allows the buffer to thoroughly soak the filter so you elute more DNA.

12. Place the miniprep column and microcentrifuge tube in the centrifuge and note the position number. The TA will operate the centrifuge once all groups are ready.

→ stop here

13. Following centrifugation, recover your microcentrifuge tube with the eluted DNA. Discard the miniprep column.

14. Add 6 µl of DNA Loading Dye to your tube and pipette up and down to thoroughly mix with elutant.

15. Analyze elutant by agarose gel electrophoresis.

Procedure IV. Agarose Gel Electrophoresis

You will be analyzing your final products for the PCR and miniprep procedures on agarose gels. The gels contain a dye that will produce a bright green fluorescence under blue light when it associates with DNA. In addition to the PCR and miniprep samples, we will load a DNA standard, or "ladder," of fragments of known size that you can use to estimate the size of any DNA molecules in your samples.

1. The TA will set up the agarose gel electrophoresis apparatus. This will include an electrode bath (or "gel box") filled with electrophoresis buffer and a power supply.

2. The TA will place 3–4 agarose gels in the electrode bath in the correct orientation. Note that each gel has eight wells, so it is possible to load one "lane" with ladder and up to seven lanes of sample on each gel.

3. The TA will load the ladder, demonstrating proper technique for getting samples into the wells.

4. Each group should load three lanes: (1) 15 µl, positive control (pUC19), (2) 15 µl, PCR product, and (3) 15 µl, miniprep elutant. Make sure to note which samples are in which lanes.

5. The TA will put the lid on the electrode bath and turn on the power supply. You should see the loading dye moving into the gel within a few minutes.

6. Using the progress of the loading dye as a guide, the TA will turn off the power and take the gels out of the electrode bath when sufficient separation has been achieved.

7. Examine the gel on the transilluminator directly or using a camera. Sketch the results or paste a picture in your notebook.

Data Interpretation

Examine your gel to determine which "bands" of DNA are present or absent, and estimate their size in base pairs or kilobases (bp or kb) by comparing them to the fragments of known size in the ladder. Complete the data table below and answer the following questions.

Sample	Expected Size	Observed Size or Absent
PCR, *gapA*	800 bp	
PCR, *apE*	500 bp	
PCR, *invA*	300 bp	
pUC19 plasmid	3, 6, or 9 kb	
Miniprep plasmid	3–12 kb	

 Why did we include the gapA *primers in the multiplex PCR test?*

 What are the results for the apE *and* invA *markers?*

 How would you interpret these results? Do they support the hypothesis that MH1 is a strain of Salmonella, *or a different conclusion?*

 Does the MH1 strain have plasmid DNA?

ZYMO ZYPPY MINIPREP KIT, QUICK REFERENCE

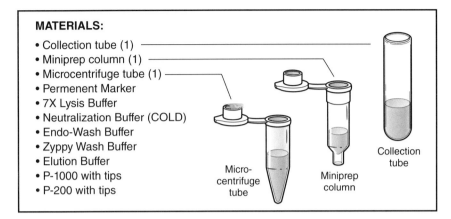

MATERIALS:

- Collection tube (1)
- Miniprep column (1)
- Microcentrifuge tube (1)
- Permenent Marker
- 7X Lysis Buffer
- Neutralization Buffer (COLD)
- Endo-Wash Buffer
- Zyppy Wash Buffer
- Elution Buffer
- P-1000 with tips
- P-200 with tips

Micro-centrifuge tube

Miniprep column

Collection tube

PROCEDURE

2. Put 600 µl cells in a micro-centrifuge tube.

3. Add 100 µl **7X Lysis Buffer**. Mix.

4. Add 350 µl COLD **Neutralization Buffer**. Mix.

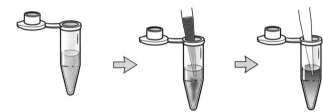

5-7. Transfer **Yellow Lysate** to a 2 ml syringe with a filter. Use plunger to filter lysate into a miniprep column in collection tube. Centrifuge.

8-12. Transfer **column** to clean **micro-centrifuge tube**. Pipette 30 µl **Elution Buffer** on center of column. Let stand 1 minute. Centrifuge to elute.

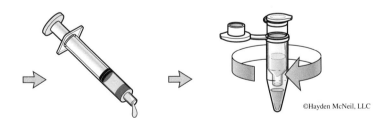

©Hayden McNeil, LLC

BSCI 105

DNA Analysis II

Demonstrating Drug Resistance in Bacteria

BSCI 105

Background

Exercise 11 directly addresses the issue of antibiotic resistance in the new strain of bacteria. At this time it is known that this strain (now labeled MH1) is resistant to the antibiotic ampicillin. To determine if antibiotic resistance is conferred by the MH1 plasmid you isolated previously, you must:

- Place the plasmid into a laboratory strain of *E. coli.*

- Culture the transformed laboratory *E. coli* in media containing antibiotics.

- Incubate the *E. coli* in different antibiotics for 24 hours to allow the bacteria to grow (if they can).

- Interpret the results of the incubation. (Incubation takes some time, and interpretation of the results will take place during the lab following this experiment.)

Be advised that the success of this experiment depends on aseptic technique. Accidental contamination of the media by airborne bacteria will negate the results. Be sure you understand the steps necessary to avoid contamination. Also, since we are dealing with bacteria, be sure to wash your hands before leaving the lab.

> **NO FOOD OR DRINK IS ALLOWED IN THE LAB.
> BACTERIA CAN ACCIDENTALLY BE TRANSFERRED INTO
> FOOD. PROTECT YOURSELF FROM CONTAMINATION!**

Procedure

1. **Fill a cup with ice.**

2. **Get two tubes of competent cells (there are 100 µl of cells in each tube) from the bucket of dry ice at the TA bench. Let the cells thaw on ice.** The cells are fragile and must be kept very cold.

3. **Label one of the microcentrifuge tubes "T" and one "NT" (for transformed and not transformed). The tubes must stay on ice.**

4. **Add 10 µl of plasmid to the "T" tube and add 10 µl water to the "NT" tube.** Gently tap the tube to mix and place on ice for 5 more minutes. (Review pipetting technique in Introduction to Equipment, "The Micropipettor" section! It is important that you pipette accurately!)

5. **While the tubes are on ice you will need to label two Petri plates "T" or "NT."** Write your group name on each plate.

6. **After 5 minutes on ice, heat shock the cells by placing both tubes in a 42 °C water bath for exactly 45 seconds.**

7. **Place the tubes immediately on ice.**

8. **Add 800 µl of growth media to each tube.**

9. **Incubate the tubes in a 37 °C water bath for 20 minutes.** This procedure allows the competent cells to stabilize and gives the plasmids a chance to produce the drug resistance proteins.

 Why do you heat shock the cells?

Why do you need the incubation step?

After the incubation period is up, you will put the cells on the plates. When you lift the cover off a petri plate, do not completely remove the cover. Simply lift the plate off at an angle (and hold it there) so that most of the plate is still covered. This prevents unwanted bacteria from falling onto the plate. All work with the plates must be done in the hood!

10. **Place 100 µl from the "T" tube onto the center of the plate labeled with a T.**

11. **Carefully remove a sterile "L" spreader from the pack in the hood.** Make sure NOT to pull any others out—if you do, don't put them back! **Lift the lid on the Petri plate and spread the competent cells around evenly on the surface of the plate.** Press firmly, but don't break the agar. Put the spreader in the waste bag when the three plates are complete.

12. Carefully add the control and ampicillin disks, placing them several centimeters apart.

13. **Change tips on the pipette. Place 100 μl from the "NT" tube onto the center of the plate labeled with an NT.** Repeat Steps 11 and 12 with a new spreader.

14. **Seal each plate** by wrapping a narrow piece of Parafilm around the edge. Your TA will show you how. Stack your plates together and label the top plate with your TA's name and section number. Give the plates to your TA, who will put them into a 37 °C incubator for 24 hours. After 24 hours, the plates will be removed and placed into the refrigerator.

 Why do the plates go into a 37 °C incubator? Why not put them in a 27 °C incubator? Or a 47 °C incubator?

 Why do the plates need to be put in the refrigerator after 24 hours?

 Why do you think the process of introducing a plasmid into a bacteria is called transformation?

 Why did you need the plate with bacteria but no plasmid?

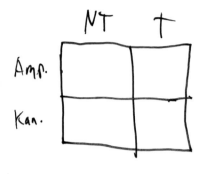

15. **During the next lab session you will examine your plates. Which plates had bacterial growth?** Measure the diameter of the clear zone around each disk. Pool your data with the rest of the class and generate averages of each treatment condition.

Plate	Antibiotic	Plasmid	Zone Diameter (mm)
T	None	Absent	
NT	None	Present	
T	Ampicillin (AMP)	Absent	
NT	Ampicillin (AMP)	Present	

Is ampicillin resistance in MH1 a genomic trait or is it conferred by the plasmid?

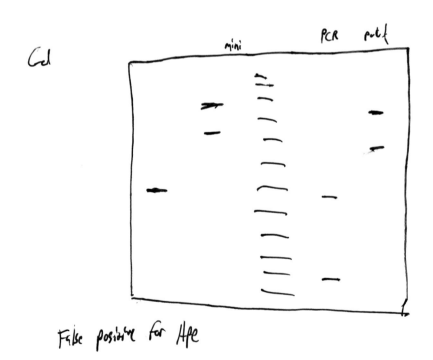

False positive for Afe

DNA Analysis III

Exploring Sequences with BLAST

Scenario

After completing the PCR tests and characterizing the basis for ampicillin resistance in the MH1 bacterial strain, you can answer one of Dr. Michroba's questions with confidence. You are sure that know the role of plasmid DNA in determining the antibiotic resistance in this strain. However, the results of the PCR tests to determine if MH1 is a strain of *Salmonella* were inconclusive. On a hunch, you repeat the PCR test on your miniprep plasmid and to everyone's surprise get a positive result for the *apE* gene. You decide the next step in your analysis should be to compare the DNA sequences of the *apE* and *lacZ* genes from MH1 to known sequences from other strains. You amplify both genes by PCR and send the products to a service to be sequenced.

Background

Determining the exact sequence of a piece of DNA has become almost trivial and can be done quickly and inexpensively using current methods. The homology or identity of a particular sequence can be determined rapidly using a program called **BLAST** from NCBI. BLAST searches for similar sequences in a large database called GenBank that is updated daily and acts as a central repository for sequence data from projects around the globe.

The BLAST program will find all known sequences that are similar to your input or query sequence, and rank them using a **similarity score** and an *E-value*. The more similar two sequences are, the higher their similarity scores will be. The E-value tells you about how likely it is to find another sequence that similar just by random chance. Search results are displayed graphically as well as through a series of pair-wise sequence alignments.

The products of many of the genes in GenBank have already been character-ized, and their structures and functions are known. By comparing a sequence with those in the database, a researcher can tell what type of molecule the gene is likely to code for. Consequently, a BLAST search can be used in a variety of investigational settings. For example, when newly cloned genes are compared with other genes that have been entered into GenBank, the researcher can infer the overall function of the new gene. In the same way, a researcher might use PCR (Polymerase Chain Reaction) to "pull out" a known sequence from a specific tissue, and use BLAST to confirm the identity of the sequence. The researcher can then make educated predictions regarding the function of this gene in her/his specific system or cell type.

In the procedure on the following page, BLAST will be used to determine the species of origin of DNA samples.

Procedure: Identifying Source of DNA

1. **Obtain nucleotide sequences for MH1 *lacZ* and *apE* genes.** These will be available from ELMs.

2. Access the NCBI Web site by typing in or choosing the following URL: http://www.ncbi.nlm.nih.gov/.

3. Once the Web site has loaded, click on BLAST in the list of popular resources on the right.

4. On the BLAST home page, skip the "assembled genomes" and click on "nucleotide blast" (under "Basic BLAST").

5. Enter a nucleotide query sequence in the window provided.

6. Choose a search set by clicking on the pull-down menu and choosing "Nucleotide Collection (nr/nt)." Change nothing else on the page.

7. Click BLAST at the bottom left and wait for the time indicated on the screen.

8. After the designated time has passed, the result will appear on the screen. **Move down on the page to where you can see a graphical representation of your results.** The top bar represents the sequence in GenBank that has the highest level of similarity (highest degree of homology) to your unknown.

9. **Click the top bar.** You will then see a text version of the results, along with the name of the species of origin, and the accession number (GenBank entry number).

10. **Click on the accession number (in blue or purple).** You will then see a bibliographic entry, which provides you with the identity of the gene and its species of origin.

11. Repeat the above procedure with the other gene sequence and complete the attached worksheet.

BSCI 105

Characterization
of Cellular Components

BSCI 105

In the previous exercises, you used bacterial transformation and agarose gel electrophoresis to characterize DNA. These are the two most commonly employed methods in the molecular biology laboratory, where scientists are often interested in studying gene regulation and function. Although genes are the ultimate source of genetic information, it is the proteins they encode and the properties of cells within an organism that actually determine function. In the next two exercises, you will apply methods that address the properties of cellular components, including organic molecules and organelles.

BSCI 105

Characterization of Photopigments by TLC

Extraction of Photopigments from Plants

BSCI 105

We mentioned previously that it is often necessary to make observations and acquire preliminary data on a given research subject before you can go on to answer further questions. Laboratory researchers are frequently required to work out the protocols (procedures), perform the studies, and make specific recommendations regarding future research. That three-part process is simulated in this exercise, where you will characterize the types of photopigments present in plant tissue samples. For this exercise, you are expected to derive a reasonable, working protocol, which you will include in your pre-lab write-up. All of the details are not provided here, so read the lab exercise thoroughly, then do a bit of thinking!

Scenario

You are a summer intern working in the laboratory of the brilliant biochemist, Dr. Yaggotta B. Kidding, at the USDA Agricultural Research Station in Beltsville, MD. Dr. Kidding is looking for ways to control the introduced menace *kudzu* that has taken over the South and now threatens Rock Creek Park. He has developed a potent new herbicide, ARSH11304, that kills not only *kudzu,* but every plant you test it on! Through various biochemical experiments, Dr. Kidding has become convinced that the herbicide acts by interfering directly with chlorophyll *b* function in the plant chloroplasts. Unfortunately, he is at a loss for how to test this hypothesis *in vivo,* because all plants require chlorophyll *b* to survive.

Your roommate is a graduate student at the University of Maryland who just happens to study the evolution of chloroplast photopigments. She suggests that you could do experiments with ARSH11304 using a variety of algae, some of which lack chlorophyll *b* entirely. You discuss this idea with Dr. Kidding, who asks you to find out more about algae photopigments and to see if you can find suitable subjects. You leave his office elated at being given such an important assignment but unsure how to proceed. You decide to begin by researching what photopigments plants use and what types of algae there are that differ in their photopigments. Armed with that knowledge you are sure you should be able to develop a protocol to compare the photopigment complements of different species and select the best candidates for further experimentation.

Before you come to lab, find out more about what types of pigments you *might* find in plants and algae.

In this exercise you will examine photopigments in plants and algae using a technique called thin layer chromatography (TLC). You will be supplied with raw extracts of photopigments and all of the materials you need to purify and separate them on TLC plates. You will be asked to develop a detailed protocol to identify the photopigments. At the end of the exercise, you should be able to predict how different plants should respond to the herbicide and make recommendations for an experimental system to Dr. Kidding.

Background
As you know, plants make food by converting light energy into sugars. This process takes place in the chloroplasts and is aided by the light absorbing properties of various pigment molecules. A plant will grow best when the pigments are given a light source that they can most efficiently absorb. However, there are various pigments that absorb different light wavelengths, and different plants have different types of pigments. Your task in this lab is to identify the pigments in different plants.

PHOTOSYNTHESIS
Review the relevant literature on photosynthesis in your textbook. Here are some of the highlights:

1. Light is captured by several classes of photopigments found in chloroplasts. The classes include chlorophylls (chlorophyll *a*, *b*, and *c*) and carotenoids (carotene and xanthophyll).

2. These pigments each absorb light of specific wavelengths, and the energy from the light is passed to specific reaction center pigments (P_{680} and P_{700}), which give up electrons.

3. These excited electrons are used to generate ATP and NADPH and H^+, which in turn provide the energy and reducing power to fix CO_2 and produce sugar.

CHLOROPHYLL AND THE CHEMISTRY OF PIGMENT EXTRACTION

Examine the structure of chlorophyll *a* below. Evaluate the physical properties of the molecule and what type of solvent system you might employ in your initial extraction of this molecule from the leaves. Be specific about the **polarity** of both the molecule and the solvent. (Hint: Remember that like dissolves like.)

Acetone is a good general solvent that dissolves many molecules that have varying degrees of **nonpolarity**. In addition, acetone can be mixed with water (80 mls of acetone to 20 mls of water) to create a solvent that dissolves mostly nonpolar molecules.

*How will you extract the pigments from the leaf? (Hint: Hexane is a **very** nonpolar substance and will dissolve only very nonpolar molecules.)*

A separatory funnel is a device used to separate different types of molecules. If you added water and oil to a funnel and mixed them well, after a few minutes the oil would move to the top of the funnel. The end result would be two layers of molecules, water in the lower layer and oil in the top layer. Suppose that we have extracted and dissolved many similar leaf chloroplast pigments into a solvent solution.

How will you separate the very nonpolar pigments (like chlorophyll) from the other more polar pigments?

CHROMATOGRAPHY

Consider a porous material (matrix) that carries pigment molecules as you run a solvent over and through this matrix. For example, imagine placing the mixture of the pigments on a long piece of paper or other similar supporting material and allowing a solvent to flow through the paper. What happens to the pigments? If the pigments are soluble in the solvent, they move along with it. The more soluble the pigment is in the solvent, the faster and farther it moves. Insoluble molecules will not move at all.

Thin Layer Chromatography (TLC) plates use silica as the porous material. The silica is the white chalky side of the plate. If a solution made of different components is spread in a dense thin line on the plate and then placed in a solvent chamber, the components will separate out along the plate. In this experiment, you can use this plate in a **chromatography** chamber to separate the pigments.

How will you separate the very nonpolar molecules from one another?

One interesting feature of TLC (Thin Layer Chromatography) is that molecules move at a specific rate along the plate. One way of quantifying this movement is to measure the distance the molecule moved and divide that by the distance the solvent front moved. This gives you a measure in R_f units (Retardation factor). For example, if the molecule moves 15 mm and the solvent front moves 20 mm, the R_f value for the molecule is 0.75. This R_f value is different for each pigment and so can be used to characterize the pigments you extract from the spinach.

Once you have isolated a pigment from other pigments, how can you determine which wavelengths of light will most effectively excite it? Any ideas?

Procedure
As part of your pre-lab write-up, write your own protocol based on the following information.

Materials available for your use in this lab (may or may not need all):

acetone (100% in repipette)	microscope slides
acetone (80% in flask)	hot water bath
hexane (in repipette)	microscope filters
cuvettes	scissors
spectrophotometer	regular funnels
test tubes	microscopes
mortar and pestle	spatula
separatory funnel	Pasteur pipettes
ring stands for separatory funnel	beakers
thin layer chromatography plates	Whatman #1 filter paper
thin layer chromatography chamber	
absorption spectra of known pigments	

Below is a rough outline to get you going; **you need to expand on the details for your turned-in protocol.** Keep in mind that you can refine your protocol later.

1. **You will obtain a raw extract of a plant or algae from your TA.** These extracts are in 80% acetone.

2. **Now that you have the pigment solution, you will need to separate the very nonpolar pigment molecules from the other more polar molecules.** How will you do this? Remember the properties of the solvents listed above. Keep track of the amount of chemicals you use.

> **DO NOT USE A SEPARATORY FUNNEL UNTIL YOU ASK YOUR TA ABOUT THE APPROPRIATE SAFETY PRECAUTIONS.**
> **YOU CAN SERIOUSLY INJURE YOURSELF OR A CLASSMATE IF YOU DO NOT KNOW EXACTLY WHAT YOU ARE DOING.**

Normally hexane and acetone are miscible (i.e., mix readily together). Why isn't the hexane mixing with the acetone? (HINT: What else is in the acetone you used?)

3. **After the last mixing, allow the separatory funnel to remain undisturbed** in an upright position by placing it in a ring stand.

 In which layer are the pigments? Why are they more concentrated in that layer?

4. **After waiting until the two solvent layers have separated, carefully draw off the lower acetone layer.** Discard the acetone into a chemical waste jar. Place the pigment mixture into a small beaker.

5. **Now, you need to separate the pigments from each other.** What will you use for this part of the experiment? How will you do this part of the experiment? Check with your TA for confirmation of your procedure. Your faithful laboratory mentor has previously covered the bottom of a chromatography developing chamber with a solvent system composed of 120 ml hexane/60 ml diethyl ether/40 ml acetone.

6. **After the plate has been run and the pigments have separated, make measurements to determine the R_f value for each pigment.**

7. Once you have recorded the R_f values, use a spatula to carefully scrape off each pigment streak into filter paper in a funnel. Add 1 ml of 100% acetone and filter into a clean, small beaker to remove the silica. Be sure to pre-wet the filter paper with acetone!

 What happens to the pigment?

8. Now that you have the separated pigments you need to determine their identity. Decide on the procedure you will use. You need to remember everything you have been taught about using a spectrophotometer (review Exercise 1 if you need to). Consider such questions as "what will your blank be?"

    There are absorption spectra of experimentally determined pigments around the room to compare to your experimental data.

9. Sketch your plate here. Draw a line over from each band: Record the R_f value and the color of the band (green, grey, yellow, gold, etc.).

Sketch of the Plate	Color	R_f Values
pencil line		

Name of species: _____

10. **Using the class data, complete Table I.**

BSCI 105

Species					
Pigments with R_f values:					

Data Interpretation

Now that you have determined which pigments are present in the plant material given to you, think about the following questions:

- What are your findings (in one or two sentences, what were your results)?

- What recommendations will you make to Dr. Kidding?

- Which species would not be killed by the herbicide?

SPECTRA

A. Chlorophyl A

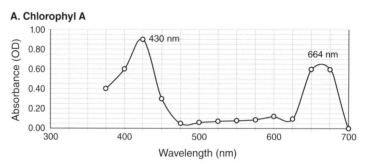

B. Chlorophyl B

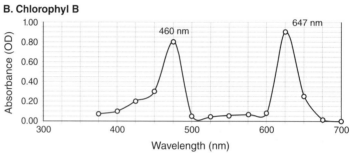

C. Chlorophyl C

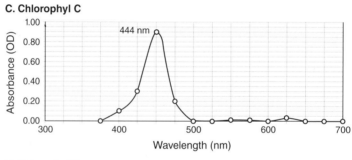

D. Chlorophyl D

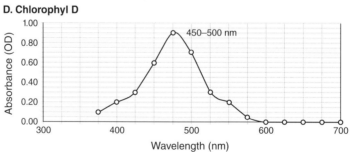

Absorbance spectra of photopigments in 80% acetone.
The expected peak wavelengths are indicated above the curves.

Deconstructing the Cell

*Understanding the Form and Function
of Cells and Organelles*

BSCI 105

> *You are Dr. Hopkins, finishing up your morning
> rounds. On your way back to your office, you stop
> by the histology lab to get the results of a liver biopsy
> you performed the previous afternoon. As you enter
> the lab, the technician is peering into a light micro-
> scope, examining slides of the biopsy. "I think the
> liver looks normal, doctor," she says, "would you like
> to have a look?"*

In nearly every discipline of biomedical science, health profes-
sionals must be able to understand and interpret biological images. In many cases this means viewing a two-dimensional image (like a piece of tissue on a slide or a series of images from
a CT scan) and mentally reconstructing a three-dimensional
structure. In the investigations you are about to perform, you
will use models, light microscopy and electron micrographs to
help you hone your ability to understand and interpret biological images. In addition, these exercises will provide you with
the opportunity to apply what you have learned about cellular
physiology and help you understand the relationship between
the morphology of cells and organelles and their function
within the body.

Before you come to class you should review your lecture
material on the following topics: cell and organelle structure,
membrane transport, cellular respiration, DNA replication,
transcription and translation, and protein modification. In particular, you should focus on the information regarding cell and
organelle morphology in the text.

The exercises you will perform today have two major emphases:

1. To teach you how to interpret 2-D images in the context of a 3-D world (i.e., what you see isn't always what you get).

2. To teach you how to interpret the possible function of a cell or organelle based on its structural and ultrastructural characteristics.

Background
CELLS AND ORGANELLES

In this lab session, we will examine the structure of a variety of organelles found in eukaryotic cells. As compared with "simpler" prokaryotic organisms (e.g., bacteria), which are small and do not contain membrane-bound organelles, eukaryotes are strikingly complex. Eukaryotes can be either unicellular or multicellular and contain a rather large number of organelles and other structural components, such as microfilaments and microtubules. Compartmentalization, with designated functions being carried out in specific organelles and/or areas of the cell, is a characteristic exclusive to eukaryotes.

Until about 1940, our knowledge of cellular organelles was sketchy to say the least. Even in the last 20 years or so, our understanding of specific structures has grown immensely. The Golgi complex, for example, has gone from a set of membranes with "little or no known function" to a complicated system involved in the processing and sorting of proteins. Building such a knowledge base begins by making observations on the morphology and location of structures within the cell. In today's lab, we will make observations at both the structural (light microscopy) and ultrastructural (electron microscopy) levels.

MICROSCOPY

Slides for light microscopy are usually prepared by embedding a small chunk of tissue (say, liver tissue) in a block of paraffin. Very thin (5–10×10^{-5} mm) slices or "sections" of the tissue are then shaved off of the block and affixed to glass slides. Frequently, the section is then stained with a dye that labels specific parts of the cells. When the slide is placed onto a light microscope, light is passed through the tissue and the internal components of the cells can be viewed. Because of the thinness of the section, the image of the tissue is essentially two-dimensional.

In transmission electron microscopy, the tissue sections must be very thin indeed, so that a beam of electrons may pass through the tissue. Consequently, tissue to be viewed under the electron microscope is embedded in a very hard plastic-like substance, so that it can be cut very, very thin (5–10×10^{-5} mm).

Again, the images you see in the transmission electron microscope are essentially 2-dimensional, and allow you to view (with great detail) the contents of a cell.

Many organelles are complex, folded structures. If a given organelle, such as a mitochondrion, folds back on itself, how will it look in a tissue section? (Hint: If you cut a bagel in half, how many round profiles of the inside of the bagel will you be able to see?)

The methods you will use today allow you to see the internal components of the cell, and require you to think about the way in which 3-D structures look under the conditions of light and electron microscopy.

Procedures

You should make your initial drawings and notations on a separate summary sheet that will be provided for you. You will also answer the questions that are posed below. This sheet should be turned in to your TA before you leave the classroom.

MODEL OF THE ANIMAL CELL

1. **Examine the model of an animal cell positioned on the front bench.** Make a sketch of each organelle listed on your worksheet.

2. Think about the function of each organelle. On your worksheet, answer the questions about the function and shape of organelles.

3. **What is the position of each organelle relative to other components of the cell?** How does the location of the organelle relate to its function?

MICROSCOPE SLIDE (AMPHIBIAN LIVER TISSUE) AND ELECTRON MICROGRAPH (MITOCHONDRIA)

Examine the section from a piece of frog liver. The tissue was treated with a stain that labels cell nuclei dark blue, mitochondria lighter blue, and structural components of the cell (microfilaments and microtubules) gray. *(Large, brown cells with blue nuclei are pigment cells—you can ignore these.)*

Cells and tissue topography at 100×:

1. **Study the tissue as a whole**—move the slide around and familiarize yourself with the different cell types present.

2. How would you determine how many cells are present in this section? What could you count? Why might this approach be limited?

3. **Locate a blood vessel within the liver tissue.** Blood vessels are seen as very large openings in the liver tissue. Some appear round while others are elliptical or elongated. **Why do some look different than others?**

Cell and organelle structure at 400×:
1. Study a random liver cell and compare it with the model. **Make a sketch of the cell on your worksheet and label the organelles.**

2. The mitochondria look like small blue granules within each cell. Liver cells have many, many mitochondria. **What does this say about the function of the cell?**

3. Study the cells lining a blood vessel. These cells are called endothelial cells and their nuclei and cell bodies are flattened and elongated. These cells also stain very dense gray in color. **What are some functional reasons that these cells would have these characteristics? (name three)**

Cell and organelle ultrastructure at 40,000×:
Examine the electron micrograph of mitochondria within a vertebrate cell. **Make a sketch of one of the mitochondria on your worksheet.**

1. Notice the numerous infoldings of membranes present in each mitochondrion. These infoldings are called "cristae." **Why would mitochondria need large amounts of membrane within the organelle?**

2. Notice that inside of each mitochondrion, there are a number of small, dense spots. These spots are concentrations of $CaPO_4$. **Why might mitochondria need such large concentrations of this chemical?**

3. Study the micrograph. **Determine how many mitochondria are present.**

Record your answers to the questions on the following worksheet and turn it in at the end of the lab.